SOURCES FOR THE HISTORY OF NURSING IN GREAT BRITAIN

edited and compiled by
Christopher Maggs
with the assistance of
Malcolm Newby

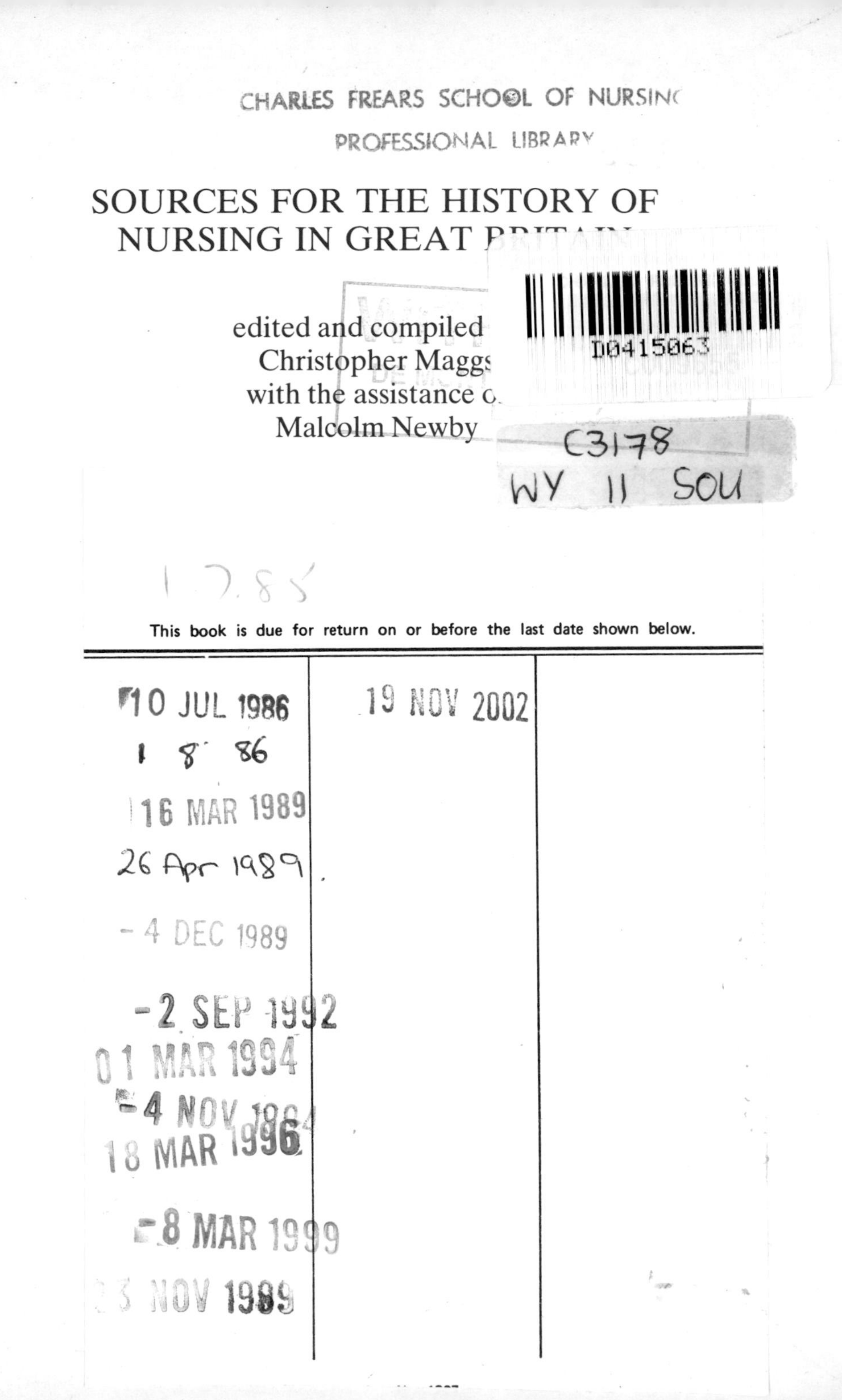

Typeset by Rowland Phototypesetting Ltd
Printed by Lithoscript, London

King's Fund Publishing Office
126 Albert Street
London NW1 7NF

Acknowledgments

The preparation of this book was made possible with the assistance of the King's Fund, London.

We would like to thank Croom Helm Ltd for permission to reproduce pages 51, 60 and 174 from Christopher J Maggs, *The Origins of General Nursing*, 1983; and the Royal College of Nursing, London, for the information in Figure 6.

Contents

Section 1
How to use this book

A. INTRODUCTION

We have produced this guide to research because we believe that there are many who are interested in the history of nursing, interested in reading about it and its context, and that some of that audience would also like to carry out research projects in the history of nursing for themselves. Often these people are held back from doing research because they feel that they are not 'historians', that they do not know how to go about finding out about the past and about nursing in particular.

There are also people who are not held back from research but who lack guidance; they are determined to pursue an interest in the past but would appreciate some help. We are concerned to address that audience as well.

Finally, there are many students, from O level or CSE, through Diploma in Nursing to under- and post-graduates who may be interested, directly or indirectly, in the history of nursing. This book will provide a reading list for them, a guide to the major areas of concern in nursing history and a guide to the contextual debates which the history of nursing should enter.

We have assumed, therefore, no prior knowledge of history or of the history of nursing, nor of the historical method. Here is a simple guide to the research method and to the major or important readings in the discipline of history which will help anyone interested in the history of nursing to develop that interest in the ways most appropriate to them.

There are two major sections: in the first section we shall be most concerned with the practice of history—the 'how to do it' part—and there are discussions on libraries, cataloguing, footnoting and the preparation of a bibliography. The second section is very much an annotated bibliography, a guide to the tremendous resources which exist for the study of the history of nursing. The third section lists some useful addresses of libraries, archives and places for help and advice as well as data.

Finally, if there is one message which we are attempting to communicate through this book, it is that any study of nursing history must fulfil two essential conditions: it must consist of an evaluation based on as wide a range of source material as is relevant to the topic and it must be set in a specific historical context, whether that context is a chronological one or whether it is a thematic one. For too long the study of the history of nursing, at least in the published material, has appeared very much as if in a vacuum. If there is to be 'history of nursing', it must accept the rigorous standards of scholarship which the discipline imposes.

B. HOW TO FIND A BOOK

B.1 Types of information

Data are available as either primary or secondary materials; primary material is, in general, unpublished or unworked and created at the time, such as diaries, manuscripts, photographs and artifacts. Some primary material may be printed, for example, minute books. In general, secondary material includes printed books, journals, and material which has been worked by someone else, such as the historian. As you will see, the distinctions between what is a primary source and what is a secondary source can, at times, be blurred and, indeed, what are secondary sources today will become primary sources tomorrow. For a useful introduction to the topic and some exercises to help make the distinctions clearer, see Section 2, 656.

B.2 Libraries

The most obvious place to begin your research is in a library; there are several types of libraries fulfilling different functions. First, the local library supplies the leisure interests of a local community, but may well have some of the basic, introductory texts you are looking for. University or polytechnic libraries generally are more specialised and cater for the teaching and major research needs of the students and staff attending them. Local reference libraries often keep material with specific local interests in mind, especially local history. Finally, there are the specialised libraries which cater, in the main, for one major interest; for example, the Library of the Royal College of Nursing concentrates on nursing topics but also keeps a selection of general history books. Some specialised libraries are connected with major institutions and service them; for example, the Library of the House of Lords.

Access to a library is not automatic; even local libraries require some residential qualification if you are to borrow books. However, most public libraries are open to everyone if they are being used as reading rooms or as reference libraries and books are not taken out.

University libraries and those of other academic institutions are for members of the institutions only, although most offer some facilities to visiting researchers. If you use such a library, you should introduce yourself to the library staff and get permission to use the facilities. In some libraries a charge is made, although this is not the case if there is a reciprocal agreement between libraries in different areas. Normally, however, visitors are not allowed to borrow material unless by some arrangement.

Specialised libraries may and often do restrict access to *bona fide* researchers and you may need to produce in advance a letter vouching for your standing as a student or researcher. This is particularly the case in the Library of the British Museum, where you have to apply for a reader's ticket to gain admission and you will be expected to state quite clearly why it is necessary for you to use that library.

In all dealings with libraries remember that librarians are trained to help you, that they are keen to see their collections used and that there is often someone on the staff with an interest akin to yours. Courtesy and respect for the skill of the librarian will often produce a more useful outcome to a visit than just turning up and randomly taking books off the shelves.

A list of some of the specialised libraries is given at the end, but it is useful to note here that the British Museum receives copies of most printed books in Great Britain and, through its reference section, has access to many more. Most of that stock is obtained through the Inter-Library Loan Service, which even the local public libraries belong to.

Before visiting a library, it is worthwhile bearing certain points in mind.

1 Check when the library is open and whether it is open to the casual user.
2 Check whether there are any special regulations in force, especially if you are using valuable or old material.
3 Do not bring food or drink into the library, and do not smoke.
4 Bring a plentiful supply of paper, index cards (see below) and pencils (including a sharpener and an eraser); it may also be useful to have a small magnifying glass and a dictionary, preferably one which gives old meanings for words as well as the modern.
5 Check whether you are able to borrow material and for how long; find out if there are photocopying facilities which you can use.
6 Walk around the library, get to know where collections are sited. Read the information sheets on the use of the library and introduce yourself to the staff, except, perhaps the busiest staff (on the issue desk, for example). There is usually someone available at a desk or booth marked 'Inquiries'.

For an excellent guide to specific libraries, including the many specialist libraries, see Foster and Sheppard (Section 2, 651).

B.3 Catalogues

Before looking in detail at some examples of special types of books, for example, Bibliographies, you should know how to find a book in a library. That is, you must understand the library catalogue and know how to read an index card. (Some libraries now use computer terminals instead of card indexes; apart from asking to be shown how to operate such a terminal, the principal information contained on such entries will correspond to one or other styles of cataloguing.) Most libraries will have three types of catalogue—the author catalogue, the classified catalogue and the subject index.

Classification systems

There are two major systems of classifying literature—the Dewey Decimal system and the Library of Congress system. The Dewey system consists of ten major 'knowledge groups', each of which is given a number—

000–099	Generalities
to 900–999	History, Geography

—and these are further subdivided to take into account more specific and specialised subjects. For example,

301.14	Social history (GB)	610.091	History of medicine
301.24	Urban history	600.091	History of technology
312	Population growth	620.091	History of technology
335.45	Chartism		

903	Dictionaries of general history
907	Study and teaching
909	World
909.82	20th-century World
930	General
941	British history
942	English history

The Library of Congress system is not as common as the Dewey system, and it uses a mix of numbers and letters to classify knowledge; thus

D	History (general), Europe, general
DA	Great Britain
DA 566–592	20th century history of Great Britain
HB	Population
HN	Social History

The important point to bear in mind when using either system is that, when you are looking for a book, make sure that you write down the catalogue number (from the index); without it you might spend fruitless effort wandering around the shelves. Figure 1 gives some examples of books in the history of nursing using the Dewey Decimal system.

The subject index

This is a simple method of giving the reader direct access to the library through its classification system. It is an alphabetical list with corresponding numbers or letters and numbers taken from the catalogue system. Since it is a simple system, it is important that, when looking for books on a particular topic, you use several of the headings. For example, nursing history may be shown under history of nursing, British history, social history, sociology or medical history. You should look through each simple heading to make sure you have found all the library collection under that heading. Figure 2 shows a typical card using the Dewey system.

The author catalogue

You may already know of an author in the area of your interest or in the general subject area. For example, Brian Abel-Smith's works on the history of the hospital and of nursing (see Section 2, 297; 422) have acquired the status of textbooks and are subsequently very well known. It would be relatively simple to find that entry in a catalogue. You can use the author to check whether the library you are using has a copy of the work, and when using this particular catalogue, you will also see if there are any other works by that author in the library, because there will be other cards there with the author's name.

You should also remember that names may sound as though spelt one way, but are actually spelt another—Smith/Smyth—and it is worthwhile noting that names of authors sometimes change on ennoblement.

Where no specific author is listed—for example, *The Science and Art of Nursing* (Section 2, 416)—the book will appear in the catalogue alphabetically by title. Similarly, if the book is produced by an organisation (for example, 308) it may appear under the name of the sponsoring organisation rather than the title. Figure 3 shows the Dewey system of author index cataloguing.

Figure 1

ABEL-SMITH, Brian A History of the Nursing Profession 1975	610.73
BALY, Monica Eileen Nursing and Social Change 1973	610.73
BALY, Monica Nursing 1977	610.78

Figure 2

Welfare State	361.6
Great Britain	361.942 360.942
Social Insurance	368.4

Figure 3

```
309.142                                              A942278

BRAGG, Melvyn

Speak for England: An Essay on England 1900-1975:
based on interviews with inhabitants of Wigton,
Cumberland

Secker & Wal.

1976   £5.50

0 436 067129
```

The classified catalogue

This catalogue is the most useful if you do not have either a title or an author's name to begin with. It helps you to find out what the library holds in the area which interests you. Having searched the subject index and found a number (or combination) for the general area of interest, you can then go to the classified catalogue and look at all the entries under that number or combination. Filed there will be the titles and authors of books which fall into that area of the classification system. You will also see a note to show where they are held in the library—for example, on the open shelves or in a reserved collection, including a short loan collection. You will also see a cross-reference to another section of the catalogue if an item is relevant to more than one area of knowledge. Figure 4 gives an example of the card you are likely to see in this catalogue.

Some special catalogues

Individual libraries often adapt the major classification systems to meet individual local needs. One library which has done so, and which the

Figure 4

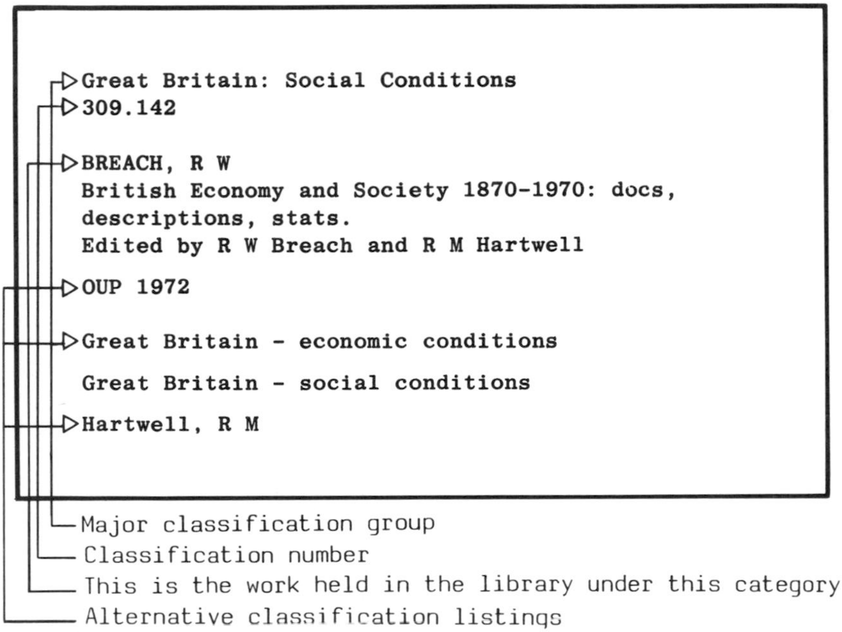

```
▷Great Britain: Social Conditions
▷309.142

▷BREACH, R W
 British Economy and Society 1870-1970: docs,
 descriptions, stats.
 Edited by R W Breach and R M Hartwell

▷OUP 1972

▷Great Britain - economic conditions

 Great Britain - social conditions

▷Hartwell, R M
```

Major classification group
Classification number
This is the work held in the library under this category
Alternative classification listings

researcher in the history of nursing will probably use, is the library of the Royal College of Nursing, London. The system in use there uses a combination of letters and numbers adapted from the Library of Congress system. Figure 5 shows an example from that catalogue of a book on the history of nursing.

Most medical libraries and libraries holding significant deposits of medical literature have a modified Library of Congress cataloguing system. In general the Library of Congress systems runs out at letter 'S'; in the medical libraries, 'Q' is pre-clinical medicine, while 'W' is medicine. In this modified system, the number '11' always stand for 'history of . . .', thus WA 11 is the history of public health, because WA is public health. Other examples include

Figure 5

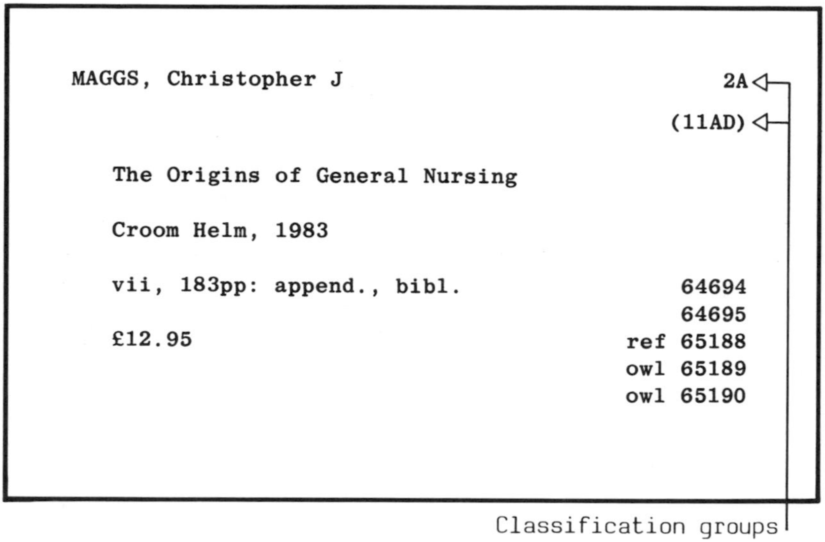

MAGGS, Christopher J
2A
(11AD)
The Origins of General Nursing
Croom Helm, 1983
vii, 183pp: append., bibl.
£12.95
64694
64695
ref 65188
owl 65189
owl 65190
Classification groups

Figure 6

2A
(11AD)
classification number
610.73
MAGGS, Christopher J
author
BALY, Monica
The Origins of General Nursing
title
Nursing
Croom Helm 1983
publisher/date
Batsford 1977
vii 183pp
pages
append
appendix
£3.50
bibl
bibliography
£12.95
ISBN
0 7134 2222X
64694
64695
accession number
A 956011
65188 ref
reference only
65189 owl
65190 owl
one week loan only

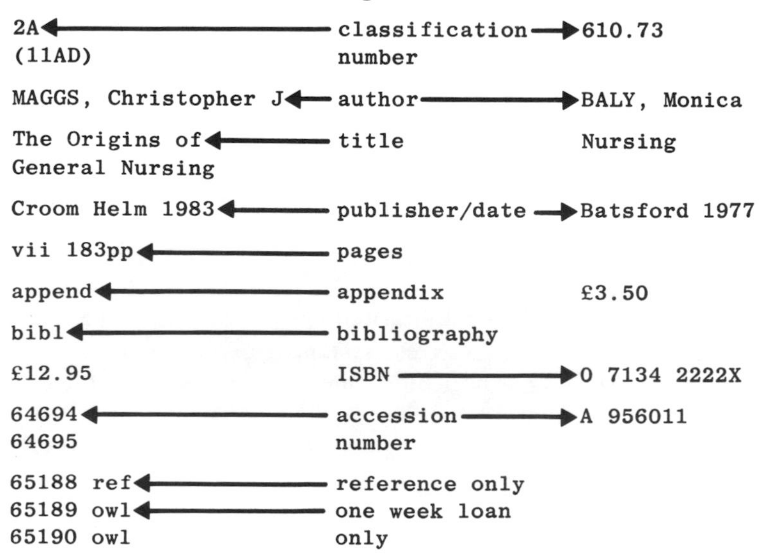

WA 30	Medical sociology
WA 100	Epidemiology
WX 11	Nursing, history of
WZ	Medicine, history of

It is also important, besides knowing what system is being used, to understand what is written on the cards in the catalogue. Figure 6 shows a typical entry using the Dewey system and a typical entry using the Royal College of Nursing system.

B.4 Note-taking and indexing

Having discovered how to use a library, its classification system and its facilities, you are now able to make use of its stock in your research. As we have stressed, methodical application in the research stage will save time later on and will help to produce a scholarly report—no matter what form that might take. We shall discuss the mechanics of reading below; here we are concerned to cultivate a methodical approach to recording material which we have used in research.

It is very important that you keep some record of works consulted, whether archive data, books or journal articles. Not only will this ensure that you do not duplicate effort, it will also help when the time comes to produce notes and references or an index at the end of your research report. A good method to be adopted is to note on your own index card the information on the card in the library, or its equivalent in the book or journal you are using. Record cards build up into a useful collection if maintained; you can also use the cards to note some of the points of interest about the work which will help you when you come to refer to the card again. These aide memoirs will not substitute for full note-taking, but provide a quick reference into the subject. Figure 7 shows two typical cards.

When using primary data or specialist data such as Parliamentary papers, it would be useful to note where the material was found, the date it was read, and any special classification numbers which were used. For example, papers originating from the Crown 'by command'—for example, *Departmental Committee on Nursing the Sick Poor in Workhouses*, 1902—are sometimes followed by a Command Number—in this example,

Figure 7

BRAYBON, Gail — Women Workers in the First World War (Croom Helm, 1980)

Useful chapter at start on women's work pre-1914. Largely on attitudes to female workers in wartime from labour, employers, govern. etc. How constant interaction between role as workers and within home affected assumptions about problems, solutions, etc. Some material on where women worked and a summary on how far war led to lasting changes for female w workers. A small piece of oral evidence from female munitions workers and how they felt about their work.

(July 1981)

BURSTYN, Joan N — Victorian Education and the Ideal of Womanhood (Croom Helm, 1980)

Main aim of book is to discuss the opposition to the expansion of women's education. All opponents using some form of 'ideal women' - biols, drs, clergy, etc. Very useful Introduction about what education existed for women (ch 1) and why women increasingly wanted to extend provis. Also discusses how they didn't all have the same aims in mind in these demands.

(October 1981)

Cmnd 1366. This number should be recorded as you consult the material; however, if you use microfilmed or microfiched copies of the original documents, you may find the numbers do not necessarily correspond. It is perhaps more important in this case, to cite (that is, record or refer to) these papers by short title and by session and volume number. Thus, our example would be recorded as *Dept. Comm. on Nursing the Sick Poor in Workhouses*. 1902. xxxviii. (Read at the Library of the University of Bath, May 1979.)

C. HOW TO READ A BOOK

(Note: many of the following comments also apply to journal articles.)

C.1 Why read other books

There are many reasons for reading a history book; from the simple pleasure gained in finding out about the past from the work of a specialist author to recording statistical information which would be difficult or unnecessary for you to collect yourself. The following list is not exhaustive but indicates some of the reasons why we need to consult secondary published and unpublished works when doing a project in history.

1 The book is a similar study; for example, of a hospital or nurse training school. We would like to know how the subject was approached, what sources were found, how it was presented.
2 The work points out the current state of historical debate or gives an insight into the issues with which your own research might be concerned. Such works may deal with problems of method or evidence, for example, the use of oral testimony.
3 The work is a background study dealing with, for example, the same topic but in a different time period or for a different group of participants. For example, there may be a study of the medical staff of the hospital you are interested in, but your area of research is the nursing establishment; you will need to read the history of the medical staff for background information.
4 A book can give you a focus for a study of your own. You may see the gaps in an area of knowledge and set your sights on filling at least some of them through your own research.

5 The book provides, through its index, references and bibliography (if there is one), other sources of information which might be relevant to your study.
6 The work contains statistical data which are difficult to obtain or which require techniques of analysis or presentation (for example, computer-assisted analysis) which are beyond your needs or competence. The book can offer a short-cut; but beware of using such data without corroborative material.
7 It may provide you with general information about the time period or theme of your own study. For example, it is perhaps impossible to understand the development of the Poor Law nursing service without an understanding of social policy.
8 Reading other writers helps you to discover your own style of writing.
9 A book may list some archive deposits which you will need to consult.
10 The author may be someone you ought to contact for advice or discussion as you carry out your own research. Most publishers will pass on letters to authors if you do not have their address.

C.2 Note-taking

No matter why you read a book, or consult any other source, remember to make up your reference card for it and to take notes from it as you read. Whether you précis sections, chapters or even individual pages, note-taking is an essential part of the research method. If you take a direct quote from a work, you must make a note of the exact location of the quote, noting also if the author you are reading took that piece from another work (see footnoting exercise, below). Your notes should show the original source as well as the source you are reading.

C.3 Reading

Techniques for reading depend very much on the reason for reading; if, for example, you are looking for specific 'facts' as statistics or for an introduction to a particular personality, such as Mrs Bedford Fenwick, much the easiest way to use the book is by looking at the index, the contents page and the preface. These sections of the book should give you an indication of how the book is organised, what issues it is addressing and the particular pages or chapters which deal with your query. Unless it is necessary to read the entire book—because of its crucial role in the topic—you will have, in the interests of time and clarity of research method, to adopt a reading method which does not always involve a complete line-by-line, page-by-page exercise. By maintaining a record system of what you have read and what the work consisted of (see above), you will always be able to return to a work at a later stage, should you need to.

D. FOOTNOTING AND REFERENCES

Footnotes and references are included in scholarly works not merely to demonstrate the range of the method used but also to show the reader how a point was arrived at using the evidence presented. The reader could, then, check that evidence and test the author's conclusion. In the natural sciences the analogy would be scientific verification and the replication of the experiment: the historian must also allow his evidence and his conclusions to be scrutinised and checked for reliability.

It is also important that the source of information is acknowledged; some evidence is considered 'superior' to others (see Marwick (656) pages 24–29 for a discussion of the hierarchy of sources); it is also important to acknowledge that another author has carried out some of the process by which you arrive at your conclusion; finally, failure to acknowledge the source of your evidence could lead you open to criticisms of plagiarism—using other authors' work without admitting to doing so.

Style of presentation of footnotes and references vary from institution to institution, library to library and publisher to publisher; all, however, share an internal consistency which you should also aim for in your own written work. The basis of good footnoting is in the note-taking and reading stage, and the card-indexing you should be maintaining. As you prepare your report is not the time to wonder where a particular quote or idea came from.

One way to find out how to footnote is to look at the books and articles you are reading; notice the different styles and choose the one which suits you best. Some authors like to put references and footnotes on the page of text to which they refer, others at the end of each chapter and others at the end of the complete work. Bear in mind your reader, and you as a reader; did you find it most useful to have this corroborative information on the page you were reading, or at the end of the chapter; was it irritating to have to thumb through many pages to find out what evidence the author had for a statement? If you intend to publish your study, it is useful to adopt the style of presentation of the publisher or journal you are intending to approach. Write to the journal or publisher and ask for their 'house style' information. Finally, there are several guides to styles of presentation and these are generally available in reference libraries. (For example, K L Turabian. *A Manual for Writers of Research Papers, Theses and Dissertations*. 1937. British edition 1982.)

The following extract will help to show how and when to footnote; remember, however, it is only one of many methods and you should check any differences between it and the style you adopt.

D.1 Footnotes: an example

(The extract, Figure 8, page 22, is taken from Christopher J Maggs. *The Origins of General Nursing*, 1983. For the listed footnotes, see Figure 9, page 23.) Points to bear in mind:

a. The number of the footnote comes at the end of a sentence or clause; for example, footnote 57 in the text.
b. The first time a work is cited it must be given in full, including author, title, date of publication and page number. Some styles include the publisher and place of publication.
c. Subsequently, the same work may be cited as 'op cit'—'already cited'—for example, Maggs, op cit p 25. It is preferable to use a short title, however, for example, Maggs. *Origins*. p 25. See footnotes 58 and 61.
d. Ibid is used when the same work is cited in consecutive footnotes, for example, footnotes 44 and 45. If the reference is exactly the same, including page number, then only Ibid is used; if the page numbers are different, they must be shown.
e. The title of a book and the name of a journal or newspaper are underlined or italicised.

f. If an author is citing another previous work, you must make this clear in your reference. For example, *National Review*, April 1863 quoted by H M Lynd. *England in the Eighteen-Eighties*. 1945. p 250.
g. Direct quotes must be footnoted.
h. Views (even when paraphrased) expressed by an author must be footnoted.
i. Additional information which would interrupt the flow of the main text should be footnoted; this may include non-essential definitions, for example, 'culture', or additional statistical data.
j. You may wish to list other authors who deal with a point you have touched upon but in more detail.

E. PREPARING A BIBLIOGRAPHY

Not all authors include a bibliography in their report or book and it is not the convention to do so in an article. This may be because of the style used by the publishers, or it may be that the author attempts to provide a bibliography through clear footnotes and references; some authors just do not bother. It is good method and practice to show the reader where you found the evidence which you have used in your discussion, but it is equally important to indicate those works which informed and coloured that discussion, but which are not directly cited in footnotes; that is one function of a bibliography.

A good bibliography will also show that your method has been correct and that you are 'up-to-date' with the latest literature. An informed bibliography, even if it is selected, will also help the reader of your work discover some of the data you used: like some of the sources you used originally, your bibliography may stimulate someone else to carry out a research project.

Three basic approaches may be made to the contents of a bibliography. First, it can list all the material you have consulted in one way or another; second, it can list a selection of the more important sources used; and third, it can take the form of a critical guide to the reading in the topic area, making a very useful contribution to historiography.

Figure 8

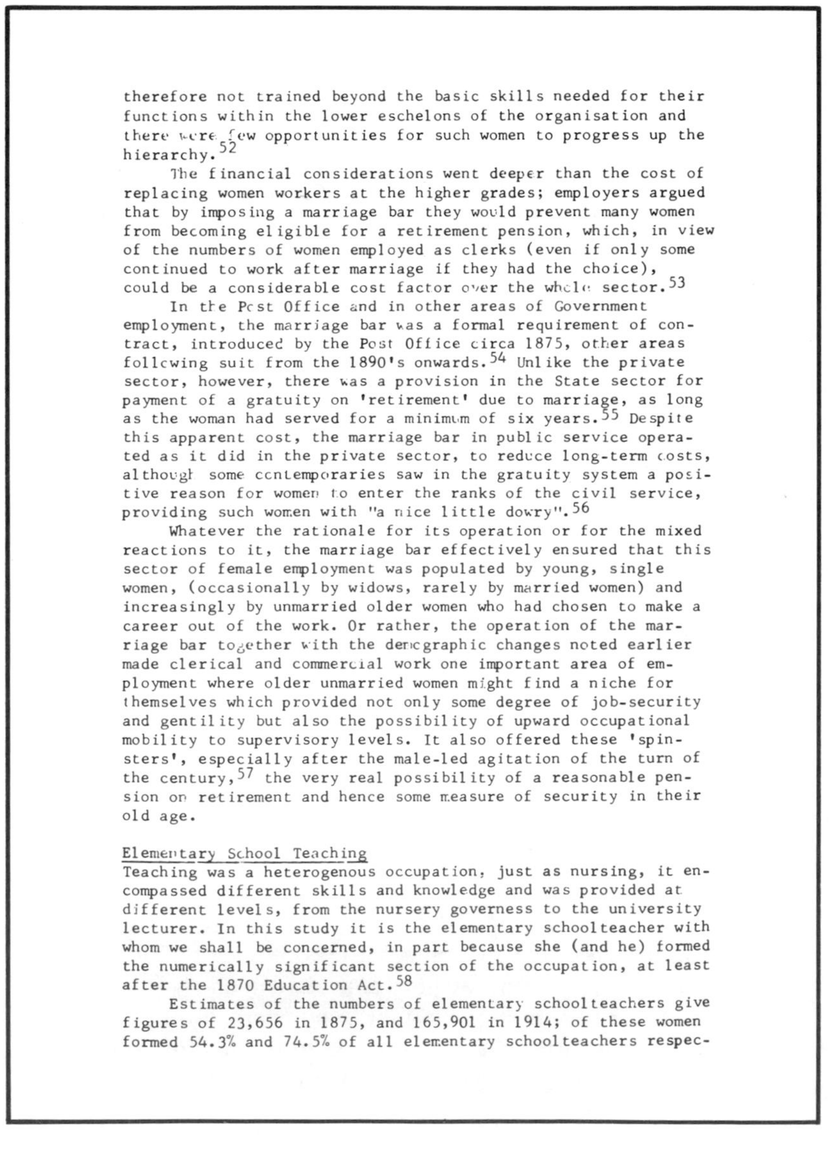

therefore not trained beyond the basic skills needed for their functions within the lower eschelons of the organisation and there were few opportunities for such women to progress up the hierarchy.[52]

The financial considerations went deeper than the cost of replacing women workers at the higher grades; employers argued that by imposing a marriage bar they would prevent many women from becoming eligible for a retirement pension, which, in view of the numbers of women employed as clerks (even if only some continued to work after marriage if they had the choice), could be a considerable cost factor over the whole sector.[53]

In the Post Office and in other areas of Government employment, the marriage bar was a formal requirement of contract, introduced by the Post Office circa 1875, other areas following suit from the 1890's onwards.[54] Unlike the private sector, however, there was a provision in the State sector for payment of a gratuity on 'retirement' due to marriage, as long as the woman had served for a minimum of six years.[55] Despite this apparent cost, the marriage bar in public service operated as it did in the private sector, to reduce long-term costs, although some contemporaries saw in the gratuity system a positive reason for women to enter the ranks of the civil service, providing such women with "a nice little dowry".[56]

Whatever the rationale for its operation or for the mixed reactions to it, the marriage bar effectively ensured that this sector of female employment was populated by young, single women, (occasionally by widows, rarely by married women) and increasingly by unmarried older women who had chosen to make a career out of the work. Or rather, the operation of the marriage bar together with the demographic changes noted earlier made clerical and commercial work one important area of employment where older unmarried women might find a niche for themselves which provided not only some degree of job-security and gentility but also the possibility of upward occupational mobility to supervisory levels. It also offered these 'spinsters', especially after the male-led agitation of the turn of the century,[57] the very real possibility of a reasonable pension on retirement and hence some measure of security in their old age.

Elementary School Teaching

Teaching was a heterogenous occupation, just as nursing, it encompassed different skills and knowledge and was provided at different levels, from the nursery governess to the university lecturer. In this study it is the elementary schoolteacher with whom we shall be concerned, in part because she (and he) formed the numerically significant section of the occupation, at least after the 1870 Education Act.[58]

Estimates of the numbers of elementary schoolteachers give figures of 23,656 in 1875, and 165,901 in 1914; of these women formed 54.3% and 74.5% of all elementary schoolteachers respec-

Figure 9

42. Holcombe, Victorian Ladies at Work, p. 146; Davin, 'Telegraphists', pp. 8-9.
43. Davin, 'Telegraphists', pp. 7-9.
44. Ibid., pp. 7-9.
45. Ibid., pp. 7-9.
46. Ibid., p. 9.
47. Ibid., p. 9.
48. Ibid., p. 9. See also, B. Hutchins, 'An Enquiry into the Wages and Hours of Work of Typists and Shorthand Writers', Economic Journal, XVI, September 1906, pp. 445-9.
49. Davin, 'Telegraphists', p. 9.
50. Ibid., p. 8.
51. Holcombe, Victorian Ladies at Work, pp.198-202.
52. Ibid., pp. 148-152; Strachey, Careers, pp. 59-60.
53. Davin, 'Telegraphists', p. 8; Holcombe, Victorian Ladies at Work, p. 178; H. Martindale, Women Servants of the State 1870 - 1938: A History of Women in the Civil Service (Allen and Unwin, London, 1938), pp. 147-9.
54. Holcombe, Victorian Ladies at Work, p.178, Mrs. Phillips (editor), A Dictionary of Employments Open to Women (Women's Institute, London, 1898), p. 112.
55. Holcombe, Victorian Ladies at Work, p. 178; M. Meredith, 'Women in the Civil Service: Part 1', The English Woman, 31, (1), July 1911, p. 38.
56. Meredith, 'Civil Service', p. 38; Holcombe, Victorian Ladies at Work, pp. 178-9.
57. Holcombe, Victorian Ladies at Work, pp. 156-62, pp. 179-93.
58. This Act was the first indication that the State was prepared to take on "the responsibility of placing an elementary education within reach of all". Part of that process was the creation of a new grade of teacher, the elementary school teacher. Holcombe, Victorian Ladies at Work, pp. 29-30; A. Tropp, The School Teachers (Heinemann, London, 1957), pp. 103-7; G. Partington, Women Teachers in the 20th Century in England and Wales (N. F. E. R., Windsor, 1976), p. 1; W. J. Reader, Professional Men: The Rise of the Professional Classes in Nineteenth-Century England (Weidenfeld and Nicolson, London, 1966), p. 181; Dilke, Women's Work, p. 8.
59. Holcombe, Victorian Ladies at Work, p. 34, p. 203; Partington, Women Teachers, pp. 1-3.
60. Partington, Women Teachers, p. 1; Holcombe, Victorian Ladies at Work, p. 35.
61. Partington, Women Teachers, p. 1.
62. Ibid., p. 1.
63. Holcombe, Victorian Ladies at Work, p. 36; Partington, Women Teachers, p. 1.
64. Partington, Women Teachers, p. 2; Holcombe, Victorian Ladies at Work, p. 36; Tropp, School Teacher, p. 187.
65. Partington, Women Teachers, p. 2.
66. A. Oram, 'The Employment of Women Teachers 1910 -

Whichever approach you decide upon, layout of the bibliography is generally the same. A bibliography is an alphabetical list of sources divided into manageable sections. These sections may be divided into primary and secondary sources; into books, articles and theses; into manuscript and published sources, or some combination of these. One factor which will determine the style of presentation, apart from scholarship, will be the length of the manuscript devoted to the bibliography. A minutely detailed bibliography could take up as much, if not more, typescript than one of the chapters making up the study. The general guideline in constructing a bibliography should be to achieve clarity, relevance to the topic and discussion and consistency of approach. Reproduced in Figure 10 is an example of a selective bibliography: the original bibliography for the thesis from which it is taken ran to 45 pages of A4 typescript; this example comes from just six pages in a book.

F. REFERENCE WORKS

F.1 Bibliographies

A bibliography, as we have already seen, is simply a list of books, works or material; the contents and standard of each vary enormously but all are invaluable aids to research. You must be aware from the beginning, however, of the limitations of any bibliography. This may be a subject limitation, for example, with only a narrowly-defined subject matter being included. It may be a geographical or ethnic or linguistic limitation, some bibliographies dealing only with books in English, or with works connected with Europe. Limitations may be made on the type of material included and some bibliographies only list printed books and not, for example, articles in learned journals. Finally, bibliographies are quickly out of date or perhaps are deliberately only addressing a specified time period, as books produced in that time or about that period.

The most important and readily available types of bibliographies are the British Books in Print trade catalogues; Books in Print catalogues; National Bibliographies; published library catalogues; subject bibliographies and the 'bibliographies of bibliographies'.

Figure 10

SELECT BIBLIOGRAPHY

A complete bibliography is given in C. Maggs, 'Aspects of the Recruitment, Training and Post-Certification Experiences of General Hospital Nurses in England 1881 - 1914, Ph.D., University of Bath, 1980.

Government Publications

Select Committee on the Metropolitan Hospitals, PP 1890/1, xiii
Select Committee on Registration of Nurses, PP 1904, vi
Select Committee on Registration of Nurses, PP 1905, vii
Royal Commission on the Poor Laws, PP 1909, xxxvii
Census of Population, 1921

Journals

American Journal of Nursing
British Journal of Nursing
The Hospital
The Lancet
Medical Press and Circular
Nursing Mirror
Nursing Record
Nursing Times
Nursing World and Hospital Review
Poor Law Officers Journal
Trained Nurse and Hospital Review
Westminster Review

Books, Articles and Theses

B. Abel-Smith, A History of the Nursing Profession (Heinemann, London, 1960)
J. J. Abraham, The Night Nurse (Chapman and Hall, London, 1913)
G. Anderson, Victorian Clerks (Manchester University Press, Manchester, 1976)
—— 'The Social Economy of Late Victorian Clerks' in G. Crossick (editor), The Lower Middle Class in Britain 1870 - 1914 (Croom Helm, London, 1977)

Figure 10 *continued*

P. Atkinson, Kind Hearts and Curettes, New Society, 27 July 1972
E. Bagnold, A Diary Without Dates (Heinemann, London, 1918)
H. Balme, A Criticism of Nurse Education (Oxford University Press, Oxford, 1937)
M. Baly, Nursing and Social Change (Heinemann, London, 1973)
J. A. Banks, Prosperity and Parenthood (Schoken, London, 1954)
E. Barritt, 'Florence Nightingale's Values and Modern Nursing Education', Nursing Forum, 12, 1, 1973
E. C. Barton, The History and Progress of Poor Law Nursing (Law and Local Government Publications, London, 1926)
F. Basch, Relative Creatures (Allen, Lane, London, 1974)
P. Branca, 'Image and Reality: The Myth of the Idle Victorian Woman' in M. Hartman and L. W. Banner (editors), Clio's Consciousness Raised (Harper, New York, 1974)
—— Silent Sisterhood (Croom Helm, London, 1975)
—— Women in Europe since 1750 (Croom Helm, London, 1978)
M. J. Brightfield, 'The Medical Profession in Early Victorian England as depicted in the novels of the period 1840 - 1870', Bulletin of the History of Medicine, XXXV, 1961
V. Brittain, Testament of Youth (Gollancz, London, 1933)
W. Brockbank, The History of Nursing at the Manchester Royal Infirmary (Manchester University Press, Manchester, 1970)
C. Bronte, Shirley, (1849) (Penguin, London, 1979)
F. F. Brooks, Nursing in Many Fields (Johnson, London, 1977)
L. Broom and J. H . Smith, 'Bridging Occupations', British Journal of Sociology, XLV, (4), December 1963
H. C. Burdett, Hospitals and the State (Churchill, London, 1881)
—— Hints in Sickness: Where to Go and What to Do (Kegan Paul, Trench, London, 1883)
—— Burdett's Official Directory of Nurses (Scientific Press, London, 1898)
—— The Nursing Profession: How and Where to Train (Scientific Press, London, 1899)
—— How to Succeed as a Trained Nurse (Scientific Press, London, 1913)
R. N. Carey, Merle's Crusade (Religious Tract Society, London, 1889)
M. Carpenter, 'The New Managerialism and Professionalism in Nursing' in M. Stacey et al (editors), Health Care and the Division of Labour (Croom Helm, London, 1977)
—— 'Asylum Nursing before 1914: A Chapter in the History of Labour' in C.Davies (editor), Rewriting Nursing History (Croom Helm, London, 1980)
S.B. Carter, A New Deal for Nurses (Gollancz, London, 1939)
L. Cazamain, The Social Novel in England 1830 - 1850 (Routledge and Kegan Paul, London, 1973)
C. Collet, 'The Collection and Utilisation of Official Statistics bearing on the extent and effects of the Industrial Employment of Women', Journal of the Royal Statistical

Of these, the two most useful at the start of research are—

1 *The British National Bibliography* (BNB): arranged under the Dewey Decimal system into author and title index and subject index, it is printed weekly with annual compilations. This bibliography lists works being produced or produced in recent years, that is, since 1950.
2 *The British Museum General Catalogue of Printed Books*, issued by the Reference Division of the British Library. The volumes list works up to 1955, then as a *Supplement* list works up to 1970; thereafter, published under the title *British Library General Catalogue of Printed Books*. This is a most valuable bibliography for works published from 1800 and is widely available in reference libraries. The catalogue is divided by author alphabetically, although there are some important and discrete sections, for example, London. One important advantage of this bibliography is that it not only lists works by an author but works about the author. You should bear in mind, however, that the name by which you know an author may not be the same as the name under which they appear in this bibliography. It is a difficult catalogue to use, at times, with the constant need to cover all the nuances of both name and topic in order to exhaust the potential listings.

There are numerous serial publications in historical bibliography which you may need to consult, including the *Annual Bulletin of Historical Literature* published annually since 1911 by the Historical Association and the *Bibliography of Historical Works Published in the United Kingdom* produced by the Institute for Historical Research at the University of London since 1940. There are, in addition, many annual bibliographies produced by the learned journals, including the 'List of Publications on the Economic and Social History of Great Britain and Ireland' published annually by the *Economic History Review*.

A more specialised but infrequent bibliography appears in the *Bulletin of the Society for the Social History of Medicine*. The Royal College of Nursing Library provides an updating of the original *Bibliography* started by Thompson (see Section 2, 389) and has references to nursing history. Recently, the new *Bulletin of the History of Nursing* has attempted to list recent works in the history of nursing.

You should also remember that published works, whether articles, pamphlets or books, are in themselves bibliographies and you should note sources in the works you read which are relevant to your interest. A list of the major bibliographical sources in history is given in Susan Lacey and Norman McCord, *British History 1760–1960: A Guide to Sources of Information*, 1979. In Section 2 we list those bibliographies which are most relevant to each sub-division; at the end of this section you will find a list of other bibliographies and of reference and guide books which will help you in your search for sources, both secondary and primary. At the end of the book are some useful addresses, some of which will supply bibliographical lists which may be useful.

F.2 Journals: abstracts and indexes

It is vitally important that you consult work published in the academic and practitioner journals as well as that in book form. Journals may be 'popular', like *New Society*, or practitioner-orientated, like *Nursing Times*, or finally, academic and directed mainly at a specialised teaching and research audience. A few, such as *History Workshop* and *Bulletin of the History of Nursing*, attempt to bridge the gap between academic and lay audiences.

You should not forget to read the newspapers, both national and local, where you may find some history writings. (For the use of newspapers as sources, see below.) Nor should you omit publications such as the *Listener*, the *Times* Supplements or even *Country Life*. You are likely to miss something obscure, but provided your search is methodical and thorough, it is unlikely that you will miss something significant.

Finding articles can be difficult; not every library carries relevant journals and many have to be very selective about back issues and acquiring new journals. There are several guides available to articles, including the indexes of the journals themselves; for example, *Current Contents: Arts and Humanities* 1979 onwards. There are also the specific listing publications, the abstracts or indexes. Abstracts not only list material, they also contain extracts of précis or synopses of articles; indexes tend to be merely lists.

The most important and relevant abstract for the historian is *Historical Abstracts*. This is a collection of brief summaries of articles on history subjects which have appeared in any of the 2200 journals searched. These summaries are grouped by topic or country and there is a detailed index to each volume. Since 1971 it has appeared in two parts: *Modern History 1775–1914* and *Twentieth Century 1914–Present*. There is an annual index and a cumulative index every five years.

To use the *Historical Abstracts* is relatively simple; first, look up the topic, or person or country in the cumulative index or in the annual index. Articles are grouped under as wide a listing as possible. For example:

History, Teaching of 74 1472
1474–5 1479–80 2707–9 2715
2718 2720 2723 3008
Czechoslovakia 1483 1489
Europe 2710
France 76 3265
Great Britain 76 1473 1477
1485–6 2711 2713–4 2716–7
2719 2721–2 2724–7
Korea 1874
Latin America 1476
Netherlands 3525
Rumania 1484
United States 1473 1477 1482
USSR (since 1918) 1481

Each entry will have a reference number which refers to the summary of the article, for example, 24A: 2852

24A: 2852 refers to the volume—24, Part A
24A: *2852* refers to the running number of the abstract in that volume.

In volume 24, under abstract 2852 you will see details of the article—author, title, issue, date and pagination of the journal in which it appears. There will also be a summary of the article.

Other guides which may be of particular use to nursing historians include:

Biography Index 1947–
British Humanities Index 1962–
The Wellesley Index to Victorian Periodicals 1824–1900, 1966
Arts and Humanities Citation Index 1978–
Social Sciences Citation Index 1969–

F.3 Theses, dissertations, newspapers

One constant complaint of the researcher is the isolation which they feel. They feel that they are the only person working in a particular area or on a particular topic, that they have no one with whom to talk and discuss their interest or to exchange ideas; they often feel that they are the only person who has problems with the research method or with writing up their work.

Some of this sense of isolation is inevitable—part of a desire to break new ground, to do original research—which may mean that the researcher is 'alone' in the field. To a great extent, however, that isolation may be counter-productive to the research as well as to the well-being of the researcher. To work in isolation can mean that the results of research will not be as rich as they ought to be, and can be, if there is contact between workers in related fields. One obvious way this isolation can be overcome is for the researcher to join history associations and societies—either the local history group or nationally-organised ones, such as the Society for the Social History of Medicine or the Social History Society. Membership of such groups means at the least receiving a fairly regular stream of group news and information; it may mean attending conferences and symposia, and even contributing papers to such gatherings.

Another way in which the sense of isolation may be overcome is to know whether anyone else has a similar research interest, either currently or in the past. The easiest way to find this out, at least as far as formal research interests are concerned, is to look at the guides to research theses in progress and completed. There are three main publications which will help you: first, the *Retrospective Index to Theses of Great Britain and Ireland 1716–1950: Volume 1: Social Sciences and Humanities*, 1975–77.

This will be particularly relevant if you suffer from the feeling that what you are doing *must* have been done before. *University Degrees in the United Kingdom: Part 1: Theses Completed* will tell you whether your topic has been covered already (an unlikely event) and *Part 2: Theses in Progress* is particularly useful for finding out what the current research interests are in your area. Finally, there are other collections which may be of help in finding out whether someone else is working on a similar topic, including the *Social Science Research Council Newsletter* and *Research in British Universities, Polytechnics and Colleges: Volume 3: Social Sciences* 1982. You should also consult *Medical Sociology in Britain: A Register of Research and Teaching*, edited and compiled by S Arber, 1978. There are several abstracts of theses and dissertations available, and perhaps the most useful will be *Dissertation Abstracts International* 1938–, of which Part A is concerned with the humanities and social sciences and Part C with doctoral theses submitted in Europe.

If you find a thesis or dissertation relevant to your study, you should attempt to read it. Not only will you learn something more about the subject, you will also see how another researcher has, successfully, dealt with pulling the research together. The thesis will also be a bibliographical guide to the topic, including perhaps new and relevant primary sources.

Theses are normally held in the library of the awarding institution, although there is a unique collection of theses dealing with all aspects of nursing, including the history of nursing, at the Royal College of Nursing—the Steinberg Collection (see Section 2, 483). Obtaining theses through inter-library loan may take time, and some theses are not available for loan to other libraries. It may be necessary to visit the holding library to consult a thesis and it may be necessary to obtain written permission of the author first. Occasionally, theses are printed on microfilm and you should make sure that the library you are intending to read the thesis in has facilities for reading film.

Finally, do not despair if you think that someone else has had the same idea for research as you; it is hardly likely that any two researchers will have the same questions in mind, use the same material or present exactly the same project from the same viewpoint. If the worst does happen, you will obviously have to look at your topic again. But you could console yourself with the knowledge that your idea for a topic was worthwhile, since someone else saw the need for it.

Newspapers

We have suggested that you scan current newspapers for the occasional article relevant to your topic or to history in general. You should also be prepared to look back through contemporary newspapers for the time period of your study. Newspapers are important primary sources (we include periodicals in this section) and can give valuable insights into contemporary issues and concerns. For example, it is possible to find out a good deal of information about a local hospital or local health conditions by reading newspapers printed at the time. Specialised newspapers, such as the *Poor Law Officers Journal*, will contain material directly relevant to a study in the history of nursing, but other periodicals and newspapers, including *The Lady* or the *Westminster Review*, also carried occasional articles about hospitals, nurses or nursing. A study of the 'home and family' pages or the 'women's' pages in various newspapers will tell you much about contemporary attitudes to women and to, for example, the care of children.

The largest collection of newspapers is held by the British Library at its Newspaper Library (see page 105 for the address). There is a guide to the collection: British Library, *Catalogue of the Newspaper Library*, 8 volumes, 1975. Other directories for newspapers include The Times, *Tercentenary Handlist of English and Welsh Newspapers, Magazines and Reviews*, 1966, for the period 1620–1919, and British Library, *Newspapers published in Great Britain and Ireland 1801–1900*, 1905. Trade union, political and related periodicals are being collected by the Modern Records Centre at the University of Warwick; for a guide to the deposit see R Storey and J Druker, *Guide to the Modern Records Centre, University of Warwick Library*, 1977.

F.4 Some useful bibliographies and guides

Apart from those already mentioned in the text, you may find important information about possible sources in the following works:

a. F M Codlin. *Aslib Directory: Volume 2: Information Sources in the Social Sciences, Medicine and the Humanities*. 1980.
b. C Cook and J Stevenson. *Longman Atlas of Modern British History*. 1978.
c. S Eagle. *Library Resources in London and South East England*. 1969.
d. *Encyclopaedia Britannica*. 30 volumes. Revised edition 1976.
e. J S W Gibson. *Census Returns 1841–1871 on Micro Film: A Directory to Local Holdings*. 1979.
f. *Libraries in the United Kingdom and the Republic of Ireland*. 1979. Gives addresses.
g. Library Association. *Directory of Medical Libraries in the British Isles*. 1957. (1969). Includes nursing libraries.
h. Library Research Coordinating Committee. *Guide to Admission to Libraries in the University of London*. 1979.
i. Manchester Studies Unit. *Directory of British Oral History Collections*. 1981.
j. P Morgan. *Oxford Libraries Outside the Bodleian*. 1973.
k. A N L Munby. *Cambridge College Libraries*. 1962.
l. D Parsons. (Compiler). *Mayson Beeton Collection: Subject Index to Books in the Collection: London and the Home Counties 1700–1930*. 1978. Includes works concerned with hospitals.
m. J C Rowles, A Green and L Jones. *Library Resources in South West England and the Channel Islands*. 1978.
n. Royal Commission on Historical Manuscripts. *Record Repositories in Great Britain: A Geographical Division*. 1979.
o. *Scientific and Learned Societies of Great Britain*. 1964.
p. A J Walford. (ed). *A Guide to Reference Material: Volume 2: Social and Historical Sciences, Philosophy and Religion*. 3rd edition, 1975.
(see also, sub-division 10, Section 2, page 99).

F.5 Journals

Listed here are some journals which carry articles, reviews or bibliographies which are relevant to the history of nursing:
Bulletin of the History of Nursing. 3 issues per year, 1983–
Bulletin of the Society for the Social History of Medicine. 2 issues per year, 1970–

Economic History Review. quarterly, 1927–
English History Review. quarterly, 1886–
History. 3 issues per year, 1912–
History of Medicine. quarterly, 1968–
History Today. monthly, 1951–
History Workshop. twice a year, 1976–
International Review of Social History. 3 issues per year, 1956–
Local Historian. quarterly, 1952–
Medical History. quarterly, 1957–
Oral History. 3 issues per year, 1971–
Past and Present. quarterly, 1952–
Social History. 3 issues per year, 1976–
Times Index. monthly, 1906– (previously *Index to the Times*).

Section 2
Guide to reading

INTRODUCTION

In this section we shall be concerned with some of the readily-available or important secondary sources which will help you to find your way into the context of your own project and into the major areas of discussion in the study of history.

For example, if you are looking at the way in which your own hospital or training school developed over the last 75 years, it will be necessary to have some understanding of not only the changes within nursing—Registration, for example—but also of the changing economic, political and social structures which contributed to those changes. Your own study will need to be set within a specific historical context and it will either add to our understanding of major historical developments or even argue for some revision of the macro-historical picture.

This section will help you identify some of the more important contexts in which to set your study. It will help to identify some current debates in history and show how your study may be situated in real historical concerns.

There are 10 sub-divisions used here; each sub-division is introduced by a short piece which discusses the major advantages and disadvantages of types of sources and which points towards the major concerns within each area of inquiry. As you read each, you will become aware that the divisions are somewhat arbitrary and you should be prepared to look through each sub-division to ensure that your topic is covered. For example, there are several titles in the sub-division dealing with women's history which could have been included in that dealing with nursing history (for example, 367). Works cited here are generally printed books:

where an article, thesis or even complete journal is listed, it is an indication of the central role which it plays in the particular debate. For example, Walk's article on the development of mental nursing (454) is one of the few works so far available on this subject.

You should also be aware that collections of articles are often published in single volumes united by a theme which may not immediately appear relevant to the study of the history of nursing—for example, 352. However, a glance at both the contents page and the index of such volumes will often show you why they are listed here; wherever possible, specific contributions in such volumes to the study of the history of nursing are listed in the relevant sub-division. You should be in the habit of using indexes and contents pages in order to help decide whether a book is useful or not, and this was discussed in Section 1.

1 GENERAL HISTORICAL BACKGROUND

Here the reading provides a general framework for any study in history; the works cited are concerned with general periods and general historical developments. However, a book or article may be read at different times for different reasons; for example, in the group dealing with economic change you will find a reference to Hobsbawm's *Industry and Empire* (46); that work is not only important for its contribution to our knowledge of the processes of industrialisation—including capital formation—but is very useful for the background it provides for our understanding of the consequences of the British industrial revolution on the mass of society, including the poor. It serves, therefore, to help us understand the way in which the health needs of the mass of the population throughout the nineteenth century depended very much on their role in the economy of Britain.

1.1 Political change

At first glance, the nurse-historian may well feel that 'politics' is an area with little relevance to a study of the development of nursing, especially a discrete study of a hospital or training school. Some of that feeling may be due to a sense of frustration with some of the literature in political history rather than a real understanding of the importance and relevance of political change to any study of nursing. Indeed, if politics is thought of not in party terms but in relationships between competing groups—power—then it can be seen that much of the recent work in the history of nursing is very much 'political history' (for example 422 and 441).

An example of the way in which the study of political events and development contribute to a fuller understanding of social change is shown in Fraser's work (220). Fraser made use of a study of the life of Disraeli (36) to demonstrate how contemporary attitudes to 'tory democracy' influenced the way in which one of the major political parties evolved their version of the 'welfare state'.

Finally, it is worthwhile remembering that Brian Abel-Smith wrote in the Introduction to his seminal study of the development of modern nursing that his book was 'a study of the "politics" of general nursing from 1800 onwards.' (p xi, 422).

General guides and reference works

1 L M Brown and I R Christie. *Bibliography of British History 1789–1851*. 1977.
2 D E Butler and A Sloman. (Eds). *British Political Facts 1900–1975*. 1975. David Butler has made psephology (the study of elections and voting behaviour) a major area of historical scholarship.
3 C C Cook and B Keith. *British Historical Facts 1830–1900*. A mine of useful background information and detail including electoral and political statistics, principal ministries, political parties and also notes on the economy.
4 C C Cook and J Stevenson. *The Longman's Handbook of British History 1714–1980*. 1983. This book is very useful if you need to construct chronological tables. For example, it would be possible and illuminating to put the chronology of political parties alongside a chronology of legislation concerning health and welfare (see Baly (424) Appendix 10). The volume also includes a guide to the major historical issues and debates as well as giving a guide to further reading.
5 G R Elton. (Ed). *Annual Bibliography of British and Irish History*. 1975–.

6 G R Elton. *Modern Historians on British History 1485–1914: A Critical Bibliography 1945–1969*. 1970.
7 A G S Enser. *A Subject Bibliography of the Second World War: Books in English 1939–1974*. 1977. Includes sections on nursing and medicine.
8 A G S Enser. *A Subject Bibliography of the First World War: Books in English 1914–1978*. 1979. Has sections on nursing and medicine.
9 H J Hannam. *Bibliography of British History 1851–1914*. 1976.
10 F Harcourt and F Robinson. *Twentieth-Century World History: A Select Bibliography*. 1979.
11 *International Political Science Abstracts*. Important journal published quarterly since 1952.
12 L Madden. *How to Find Out About the Victorian Period: A Guide to Sources of Information*. 1970. A useful starting place for Victorian studies. Contains some guidance to the major areas of Victorian life, including literature, religion and medicine (which includes nursing).
13 A T Milne. (Ed). *Writings on British History 1946–1948*. 1973.
14 A T Milne. (Ed). *Writings on British History 1949–1951*. 1975. Subsequent editions of 13 and 14 appeared with new editors.
15 B R Mitchell and P Deane. *Abstracts of British Historical Statistics*. 1962. Very informative data on many aspects of the economy.
16 J Roach. (Ed). *A Bibliography of Modern History*. 1968.
17 UNESCO. *International Bibliography of Political Science*. Published annually since 1954.

General works

18 A Calder. *The People's War: Britain 1939–45*. 1969. Essential reading for the background to the changing provision and attitudes to welfare and nursing services during the War.
19 A P Havighurst. *Modern England 1901–1970*. 1976.
20 E J Hobsbawm. *The Age of Revolution: Europe 1789–1848*. 1962.
21 A Marwick. *Britain in the Century of Total War: War, Peace and Social Change 1900–1967*. 1968.
22 W N Medlicott. *Contemporary Britain 1914–1964: With an Epilogue 1964–1974*. 1967 and 1975.
23 K O Morgan. *The Age of Lloyd George*. 1971.
24 H Pelling. *Popular Politics and Society in Late Victorian Britain*. 1968.

25 M Pugh. *The Making of Modern British Politics 1867–1939.* 1982.
26 D Read. *Edwardian England.* 1972.
27 R T Shannon. *The Crisis of Imperialism 1865–1915.* 1976.
28 B Waites, Popular Politics in the First World War, in Open University Course Booklet A401. *Popular Politics 1870–1950.* 1974.
29 R K Webb. *Modern England from the Eighteenth Century to the Present.* (2nd Edition) 1980. One of the major reference textbooks available; has a short but useful bibliography and is very easy to read and follow.

Political parties

30 P Adelman. *Gladstone, Disraeli and Late Victorian Politics.* 1970.
31 R Blake. *The Conservative Party from Peel to Churchill.* 1972.
32 E J Feuchtwanger. *Disraeli, Democracy and the Tory Party.* 1968.
33 N Gash. *Aristocracy and the People 1815–1865.* 1979. One of the better examples of traditional political history.
34 D A Hamer. *The Politics of Electoral Pressure: A Study in the History of Victorian Reform Agitations.* 1977. Comes very close to a comprehensive survey of the role of pressure groups in Victorian politics.
35 H Pelling. *A Short History of the Labour Party.* 1961.
36 P Smith. *Disraelian Conservatism and Social Reform.* 1967.
37 J R Vincent, The Parliamentary Dimension of the Crimean War. *Transactions of the Royal Historical Association.* Series 5. 31, 1981. This article provides the political background to the events through which Florence Nightingale operated and established her early reputation.

Government

38 D Fraser. *Urban Politics in Victorian England: The Structures of Politics in Victorian Cities.* 1976.
39 D Fraser. *Power and Authority in the Victorian City.* 1979. A study of the development of urban power through social and political reform. Useful case studies of Bristol, Bradford, Birmingham and Sheffield.
40 E P Hennock. *Fit and Proper Persons: Ideal and Reality in Nineteenth-Century Urban Government.* 1973.
41 B Keith-Lucas. *English Local Government in the Nineteenth and Twentieth Centuries.* 1977.

42 D Read. *England 1868–1914: The Age of Urban Democracy*. 1979. An excellent introduction to the processes of political change in the period. There are 31 short chapters arranged under three main sections. All aspects are touched upon, including economic, social and international history and there is a good bibliography. See also Briggs (101) and Medlicott (22).

1.2 Economic developments

Economic history is not necessarily the dry, statistical study it is often thought. You do not need any special skill in order to understand the better economic history literature, although if you are unused to the use of tables and diagrams, you might need to take some extra time and care when reading such material.

It is perhaps a truism that economic structures underpin social action: for example, it is difficult to understand how the medical services under the Poor Law came about without an earlier understanding of the pressures put upon the Poor Law systems by its critics and by its users in times of economic growth and recession.

A simpler example of the relationship between the economy and social action may be drawn from a study of the conditions of service experienced by many nurses in the nineteenth century. It would appear that nurses were poorly paid (422) and worked excessively long hours. However, this somewhat simplistic and indeed inaccurate view needs to be set in its context—the pay and conditions of service of other, similar workers. We should therefore treat such statements with caution and seek further evidence, such as that to be found in Routh (58).

Similarly, it has been argued that one factor contributing to demands for reform of nursing was the economic hardship suffered by the middle classes in mid-nineteenth century, hardship which forced more women into the work and labour markets. (344; 354; 367).

Documents

43 M Berg. (Ed). *Technology and Toil in Nineteenth-Century Britain*. 1979.
44 W H B Court. *British Economic History 1870–1914*. 1962.

General works

45 C M Cipolla. (Ed). *The Fontana Economic History of Europe: Volume 3: The Industrial Revolution*. 1973. See the article by Hartwell on the growth of the service sector.
46 E J Hobsbawm. *Industry and Empire*. 1968. One of the better accounts of the relationship between economic and social change. Written from a marxist perspective and offering insights which other writers on the topic have had to deal with, including the 'pessimist' argument about the standard of living of the working class in the wake of industrialisation. Easy to read.
47 E J Hobsbawm. *The Age of Capital 1848–1875*. 1975. The European dimension to the Mid-Victorian economy of Britain.
48 P Mathias. *The First Industrial Nation*. 1969. A standard textbook on the subject.
49 A E Musson. *The Growth of British Industry*. 1978. A comprehensive account of major changes between 1500 and 1939. It suffers somewhat from its over-long timescale.

Work

50 G Anderson. *The Service Occupations of Nineteenth-Century Liverpool*. 1981.
51 P Joyce. *Work, Society and Politics: The Culture of the Factory in Later Victorian England*. 1980.
52 P H Lindhert, English Occupations 1670–1811. *Journal of Economic History*, XL, 4. 1980.

Labour and employers

53 A L Bowley. *Wages and Income in the United Kingdom since 1860*. 1937.
54 A Chapman. *Studies in the National Income and Expenditure of the*

United Kingdom: Wages and Salaries in the United Kingdom 1920–1938. 1953.
55 E H Hunt. *British Labour History 1815–1914*. 1981. Useful but traditional approach to labour history. Full of detail about work but lacks any real analysis of the division of labour based on sex.
56 C More. *Skill and the English Working Class 1870–1914*. 1980. An important contribution to the discussion of skill and the division of labour. There is a useful first chapter which discusses some of the major issues. Suffers somewhat from a lack of 'context' and has a too cavalier approach to the 'problem' of the relationship between work, skill and women workers.
57 S Pollard. *The Genesis of Modern Management*. 1965. An essential introduction to the rise of British industrial relations and management techniques after 1750. A major contribution to the understanding of the internalisation of a work ethic.
58 G Routh. *Occupations and Pay in Great Britain 1906–1960*. 1965.

Economic change

59 J Burnett. *A History of the Cost of Living*. 1969.
60 R A Church. *The Great Victorian Boom 1850–1873*. 1975.
61 D C Marsh. *The Changing Social Structure of England and Wales 1871–1951*. 1958.
62 A S Milward. *The Economic Effects of the Two World Wars on Britain*. 1970.
63 S Pollard. *The Development of the British Economy 1914–1950*. 1962. Chapters V–VII have sections on the developments within the welfare and health systems as these were influenced by the wartime and post-war economies.
64 S B Saul. *The Myth of the Great Depression 1873–1896*. 1969. Should be read in conjunction with Church (60).
65 J M Winter. (Ed). *War and Economic Development*. 1975. A collection of essays of which two, by Mathias and Harris, are important to a study of the changes which took place within welfare and health services. Has a very good bibliography, although many of the works listed are somewhat specialised for the general reader.

1.3 Social history and social conditions

Social history was once described as history with the politics left out, but recent literature would suggest that such a perspective no longer holds true. Most writers would argue that social history (which is not the same as 'socialist history') is concerned with more than everyday actions, that its emphasis is on the structures which determine and are determined by those actions. These actions are produced by people as agents rather than as subjects of nebulous forces or 'ideals' (89). Social history is not only about 'ordinary' people, although they must be seen as historical agents as much as kings, queens and politicians: social history is concerned with relationships—of power, class and economies.

Listed here are some of the more readable works in social history; also included are works by contemporaries which provide important data for 'everyday' life which has enabled some historians to reconstruct the processes of social change and the experiences of social transformation.

Primary and contemporary works

66 Lady Bell. *At the Works: A Study of a Manufacturing Town: Middlesborough*. 1907. Reprinted 1969.
67 M L Davies. (Ed). *Life As We Have Known It*. 1931.
68 H Mayhew. *London Labour and the London Poor*. 4 volumes, reprinted 1968; originally published 1861/2.
69 M Pember Reeves. *Round About A Pound A Week*. 1913. Reprinted 1979.
70 R S Rowntree. *Poverty: A Study of Town Life: York*. 1901.

Guides and reference works

71 J Burnett. *Destiny Obscure: Autobiographies of Childhood, Education and Family from the 1820s to the 1920s*. 1982. Has some very useful introductory pieces by Burnett.
72 J Burnett. *Useful Toil: Autobiographies of Working People from the 1820s to the 1920s*. 1974.
73 A Fried and R M Elman. (Eds). *Charles Booth's London*. 1969.
74 H Hendrick. *The History of Childhood and Youth: A Guide to the*

Literature. Oxford Polytechnic Faculty of Modern Studies Occasional Papers, 1. 1981. An essential contribution to a neglected area of scholarship. A selective but stimulating bibliography with useful guides to readings in welfare and social policy as they involved children.
75 P Keating. (Ed). *Into Unknown England 1866–1913*. 1976.
76 E P Thompson and E Yeo. (Eds). *The Unknown Mayhew*. 1971.

Overviews

77 P Aries. *The Hour of Our Death*. 1981. The first full-scale study of European attitudes to death.
78 F Bedarida. *A Social History of England 1851–1975*. 1976. English language edition 1978.
79 G Best. *Mid-Victorian Britain 1851–1870*. 1971. See Harrison (86). Useful introduction; very readable.
80 N Branson and M Heinemann. *Britain in the Nineteen Thirties*. 1973.
81 A Briggs. *The Age of Improvement 1783–1867*. 1959.
82 A Briggs. *Social Thought and Social Action*. 1961.
83 A Briggs. *Victorian People*. 1965.
84 A Briggs. *The Nineteenth Century*. 1970.
85 S Glynn and J Oxborrow. *Inter-War Britain: A Social and Economic History*. 1976. One of the best accounts of a difficult approach to the study of the period. Essential reading for any student of the twentieth century.
86 J F C Harrison. *The Early Victorians 1832–1851*. 1971. See Best (79). As readable and informative.
87 P Horn. *The Rural World 1780–1850: Social Change in the English Countryside*. 1980. Has a very good bibliography and several appendices using primary data. The transition from an economy and society based on land and agriculture to one based on industry and manufacture is documented in, for example, Hobsbawm (46; 47) and Mathias (48). This study offers an analysis of the systems left behind by industrialism.
88 R W Malcolmson. *Life and Labour in England 1700–1780*. 1981. A sort of 'prequel' to Horn (87); easy to read with a good bibliography.
89 H Perkin. *The Origins of Modern English Society 1780–1880*. 1969. An important and innovative work of social history by the 'first' professor of social history in England. Much attacked for its emphasis on 'ideals' as

agencies of change and its odd analysis of class in the eighteenth century.
90 R Porter. *English Society in the Eighteenth Century*. 1982. Very much a new style social reconstruction.
91 P Thompson. *The Edwardians: The Remaking of British Society*. 1977. A mixture of sociological analysis and primary (oral) testimony from all sections of society.

Class and social change

92 A Armstrong. *Stability and Change in an English Country Town: A Social Study of York 1801–1851*. 1974.
93 C Calhoun. *The Question of Class Struggle: Social Foundations of Popular Radicalism during the Industrial Revolution*. 1982. Perhaps most useful for its summary of the major debates about the nature and role of class in social change.
94 F Gloversmith. (Ed). *Class, Culture and Social Change: A New View of the Nineteen Thirties*. 1980.
95 P Keating. (Ed). *Social Change in Victorian England*. 1980.
96 G S Jones. *Outcast London: A Study in the Relationship Between Classes in Victorian Society*. 1971.
97 S Meacham. *A Life Apart: The English Working Class 1890–1914*. 1977.
98 E P Thompson. *The Making of the English Working Class*. 1963. Arguably the most important recent text in social history which even his staunchest critics have been forced to respond to. (See, for example, Neale (136).) Makes sweeping generalisations and uses ambiguous sources but remains a seminal study of social change.
99 J Saville. (Ed). *Working Conditions in the Victorian Age*. 1973.
100 P Stearns. *Lives of Labour*. 1975. A comparative study drawing mainly on European sources.

Towns and cities

101 A Briggs. *Victorian Cities*. 1963.
102 C Foreman. *Industrial Town: Self-Portrait of St Helens in the Nineteen Twenties*. 1979. Deals with health and the Poor Law.
103 M Dorothy George. *London Life in the Eighteenth Century*. 1925. Though overtaken by, for example, Porter (90), remains a classic.

104 R Roberts. *The Classic Slum: Salford Life in the First Quarter of the Century*. 1971.
105 R Williams. *The Country and the City*. 1973. Essentially a theoretical and conceptual approach to the relationship between the two worlds of the town and the country.
106 S Thernstrom and R Sennett. (Eds). *Nineteenth-Century Cities*. 1974.

Children and the family

107 M Anderson. *Approaches to the History of the Western Family 1500–1914*. 1980. Useful 'pocketbook' which summarises recent developments in the history of the family, which itself is a recent development.
108 P Aries. *Centuries of Childhood*. 1960.
109 J A Banks. *Prosperity and Parenthood: A Study of Family Planning among the Victorian Middle Classes*. 1954. An important work which seeks to explain the pressures within and from outside which helped to shape the structure of the middle class family.
110 J A and O Banks. *Feminism and Family Planning in Victorian England*. 1964.
111 W Foley. *A Child in the Forest*. 1974. Autobiographical account of a rural working class life as seen and experienced by a female child.
112 D Gittings. *Fair Sex: Family Size and Structure 1900–1939*. 1982.
113 A McLaren. *Birth Control in Nineteenth-Century England*. 1978. A critical study of working class birth control and a counter to Banks (109; 110).
114 E Shorter. *The Making of the Modern Family*. 1975. Heavily criticised from all sides; often ahistorical and more often prejudiced.
115 J Springhall. *Youth, Empire and Society: British Youth Movements 1883–1940*. 1977.
116 J Walvin. *A Child's World: A Social History of English Childhood 1800–1914*. 1982. Timescale far too long to do justice to a complex and new area of historical concern.

Culture

117 J Burnett. *Plenty and Want: A Social History of Diet in England from 1815 to the Present Day*. 1966.

118 W H Fraser. *The Coming of the Mass Market 1850–1914*. 1981. Excellent discussion of the growth of consumerism and the spread of shops and shopping as a social event.
119 J. Walvin. *Leisure and Society 1830–1950*. 1978.
120 R Williams. *Culture and Society 1780–1950*. 1958. Examines the links between literature and social change through the published works of several authors, including Dickens, Ruskin, Lawrence and Orwell.

Fiction

121 C Dickens. *Hard Times*. 1854.
122 J Galt. *Annals of the Parish*. 1895.
123 G and W Grossmith. *Diary of a Nobody*. 1892.
124 A J P Taylor. *English History 1914–1945*. 1965. Cited here because of its selected bibliography of fiction for the post-1914 period.
125 R Tressell. *The Ragged-Trousered Philanthropist*. 1914.

History—general

Included here are works which examine and guide the reader through some of the methodologies in historical scholarship. Thus, there are several which deal with oral evidence (128; 129; 141) and others which discuss project work (126; 140).

126 G Kitson Clarke. *Guide for Research Students working on History Subjects*. 1958.
127 G Kitson Clarke. The Making of Modern Victorian England. 1962. Listed here as an example of a traditional style of history which would not be out of place in the late nineteenth century.
128 J Clarke, C Critcher and R Johnson. (Eds). *Working Class History: Studies in History and Theory*. 1979. A direct contrast to 127.
129 C Maggs, Oral history and nursing history. *Nursing Times*, October 19, 1983.
130 J Marczewski, Quantitative History. *Journal of Contemporary History*. 3 (2). 1968. Useful, easy to read guide to the use of quantitative methods in history.
131 A Marwick. *War and Social Change in the Twentieth Century*. 1974. Adds Little to Marwick (21).

132 P Mathias. *The Transformation of England*. 1979. A collection of previously published essays; see chapter 14 for a discussion of the relationship between war and public health.
133 B Mazlish, What is Psycho-History? *Transactions of the Royal Historical Association*. Series 5, 21. 1971.
134 R J Morris. *Class and Class Consciousness in the Industrial Revolution 1780–1850*. 1979. Helpful and clear rehearsal of the major competing explanations of social change and the relationships of class in society.
135 C L Mowat. *Britain Between the Wars 1918–1940*. 1955. An earlier work which has been overtaken by Glynn and Oxborrow (85).
136 R S Neale. *Class in English History 1680–1850*. 1981. An attempt to reassess marxist class analysis and to offer a 'refined' model, based on five as opposed to three classes. Interesting for its discussion of the nature of social history and for its chapter on women and class.
137 A O'Day. (Ed). *The Edwardian Age: Conflict and Stability 1900–1914*. 1979. One of the most useful chapters is that by Gourvish on the standard of living in the period which saw the emergence of 'professional nursing'.
138 S Pollard. *The Idea of Progress: History and Society*. 1968.
139 J Ryder and H Silver. *Modern English Society: History and Structure 1850–1970*. 1970. Much used by teachers-in-training as a simple introduction to the subject.
140 A Rogers. (Ed). *Group Projects in Local History*. 1977.
141 P Thompson. *The Voice of the Past: Oral History*. 1978. Important guide to the use of oral evidence in the study of history.
142 J T Ward. (Ed). *Popular Movements c 1830–1850*. 1970. Includes an article by Rose on the Anti-Poor Law Movement and another by Hume on public health.
143 B R Wilson. Sociological Methods in the Study of History. *Transactions of the Royal Historical Association*. Series 5, 21. 1971.

2 SOCIAL POLICY

As we have noted, many of the sub-divisions overlap in the topics covered. Precisely what is meant by 'social policy' is unclear, ranging from attempts by individuals or groups to bring about social change or social stability to the involvement of the State in the everyday life of its people through legislation. According to Marshall (162) social policy is not a 'technical term with exact meaning . . . it is taken to refer to the policy of governments with regard to action having a direct impact on the welfare of the citizens by providing them with services or income. The central core consists, therefore, of social insurance, public or national assistance, the health and welfare services and housing policy. Education obviously belongs but is omitted [from Marshall's work] so also is crime.' (p 7)

To examine Marshall's 'central core' means that we need to look not only at the actions or inactions of governments but at the pressures and movements for specific policies or packages of policies. A study of social policy cannot limit itself to a description of a discrete area, for example, the provision of a death grant, without also concerning itself with an analysis of the civil service, ideology, pressure group politics and the economy at least. In the following sub-division you will find many examples of this contextual approach to the study of social policy, but one example stands out, if only because it has achieved 'textbook' status, that is, Fraser (220).

2.1 Documents

144 E J Evans. (Ed). *Social Policy 1830–1914: Individualism, Collectivism and the Origins of the Welfare State*. 1978. Primary sources collected under eight topics including housing and education.
145 J R Hay. *The Development of the British Welfare State 1880–1975*. 1978.
146 P V Turner. *'Charity for 100 years': History of the Monmouth Street Society 1805–1904*. 1914. A unique collection of material from a Ladies Visiting and Distress Committee in Bath, Avon, which led to the introduction of a form of health visiting in the area.
147 B Watkin. (Ed). *Documents on Health and Social Services 1834 to the Present*. 1975. A preliminary source book with short notes on, for example, the Poor Law, Public Health and Health Services, including hospitals and nursing. A useful bibliography.

2.2 Contemporary works

148 C Booth. *The Aged Poor in England and Wales*. 1894.
149 S G and E O A Checkland. (Eds). *The Poor Law Report of 1834*.
1973. The original Report by Chadwick and others is preceeded by an Introduction by the Checklands which sets the Report and its methods in its context.
150 W Cobbett. *Rural Rides*. 1830. Reprinted 1967. A radical's reaction to the onrush of industrialisation.
151 Sir F M Eden. *The State of the Poor*. 1797. A generally forgotten record of life in many of the pre-1834 Poor Law parishes. A mass of detail about diet and income and the state of the working classes.
152 F Engels. *The Condition of the Working Class in England*. 1892. The 1969 edition has a very good Introduction by Hobsbawm.
153 A Flew. (Ed). *Malthus: An Essay on the Principles of Population 1798*. 1970. One of the major critics of the Old Poor Law, and indeed, any state provision of its kind. Malthus's influence was perhaps felt more after his death than at the time of his writing.
154 M W Flinn. *Edwin Chadwick's Report on the Sanitary Condition of the Labouring Population of Great Britain 1842*. 1965. Essential reading for the background to public health and social reform throughout the nineteenth century. Flinn's Introduction points to the thoroughness and comprehensiveness of Chadwick's study, in contrast to the Poor Law Report (1832).
155 H George. *Poverty and Progress*. 1880. Said to have been the inspiration for the resurgence of socialism in Britain in the 1880s and 1890s. Certainly attracted a good deal of contemporary attention from reformers and pressure groups and may have inspired some to attempt to refute his conclusions through 'scientific' social investigation.
156 J Simon. *English Sanitary Institutions*. 1890. The classic contemporary study of the development of public health by one of its leading proponents.

2.3 General works

157 B B Gilbert. *British Social Policy 1914–1939*. 1970. Has become a textbook. Contains a good bibliography as well as some useful brief

'biographies' of significant individuals connected with social policy in the period.
158 E P Hennock. Poverty and Social Theory in England. *Social History*, 1. 1976. A very interesting article which sets out many of the major issues surrounding the development of social policy.
159 B Inglis. *Poverty and the Industrial Revolution*. 1971.
160 K Jones. *Mental Health and Social Policy 1845–1959*. 1960.
161 J MacNicol. *The Movement for Family Allowances 1918–1945: A Study in Social Policy*. 1980.
162 T H Marshall. *Social Policy*. 1965.
163 E Midwinter. *Victorian Social Reform*. 1968. A brief but useful introduction to the subject.
164 J Roach. *Social Reform in England 1780–1880*. 1978.
165 P Thane. (Ed). *The Origins of British Social Policy*. 1978. Essential collection of articles.

2.4 Role of government and the state

One of the most important debates in recent years in the area of the history of social policy has been the role of the state and of government. Much social policy is tied up in legislation passed by Parliament, and we need to understand how that organisation determines social policy. But legislation is mediated through a bureaucracy, the Civil Service, as well as through the professional delivers of the service, for example, social workers. We need to understand the relationships which exist between the state and Parliament and that bureaucracy, the civil service.

The debate was opened by MacDonagh, in particular (171), who argued that social policy developments owed much to the creation of a group of 'experts' within the Civil Service. For MacDonagh and others sharing his perspective, 'the dynamic force behind changes in social policy is the civil service itself. It is civil servants who identify, establish and define social problems and who frame the only acceptable remedies for them.' (Hay (145) p 102). Pressure groups and extra-parliamentary action are therefore of secondary significance in the development of social policy.

More recently, this view has been criticised by, among others, Hay (145) and Harris (551); although they do not completely reject MacDonagh's basic thesis, these historians argue for a more complex relationship which takes into consideration the important role of pressure groups and reform groups. As Hay has summarised, 'Historical studies . . . tend to confirm the importance of political pressures and changing attitudes to social reform. They also suggest that institutional influences should not be neglected.' (Hay (222) p 23).

Finally, note should be taken of the article by Strachan (174); at first glance the subject matter appears to have little relevance to the history of nursing. However, Strachan's contribution to the 'MacDonagh controversy'—as it has become known—offers important parallels for the study of nursing. Its subject, military history and the role of government, shows how a field of history has been transformed by the need to take account of developments in another branch of history, social policy. The study of nursing history as social policy could, therefore, be used as another case study in the debate over the processes of social change.

166 P W J Bartrip. British Government Inspection 1832–1875: Some Observations. *Historical Journal*, 25. 1982. Continues to keep the MacDonagh debate alive.
167 R A Chapman and J R Greenaway. *The Dynamics of Administrative Reform*. 1980.
168 C Cromwell. *Revolution or Evolution: British Government in the Nineteenth Century*. 1977. Uses contemporary material to guide the reader through the debate.
169 M J Cullen. *The Statistical Movement in Early Victorian Britain*. 1975. The ways in which social policy developed in Britain owed much to the empiricist tradition, 'fact-finding', and this book traces the movement for establishing that tradition.
170 O MacDonagh. The Nineteenth-Century Revolution in Government: A Re-Appraisal. *Historical Journal*, 1. 1958. The article which first stimulated the debate.
171 O MacDonagh. *A Pattern of Government Growth: The Passenger Acts and Their Enforcement 1800–1860*. 1961. The study of these Acts led MacDonagh to present his controversial thesis.

172 O MacDonagh. *Early Victorian Government 1830–1870*. 1977.
173 H Parris. Nineteenth-Century Revolution in Government: A Re-Appraisal Re-Appraised. *Historical Journal*, 3. 1960.
174 H Strachan. The Early Victorian Army and the Nineteenth-Century Revolution in Government. *English Historical Review*, 95. 1980.
175 A J Taylor. *Laissez-Faire and State Intervention in Nineteenth-Century Britain*. 1972. A short and readable guide to the debate over laissez-faire or the role of the state in the life and economy of the country. He offers a definition of the concept which draws upon both the contemporary experiences of government intervention and on historians use of the term as a 'useful simplification' of a complex issue. The book includes short pieces as case studies in laissez-faire, including public health. The select bibliography is a good guide through much of the relevant literature.

2.5 Poverty and the Poor Laws

The Poor Laws were inextricably bound up with both the economic life of the nation and with the health and welfare of the individual. For many it was the provider of 'care' from cradle to grave, hated and villified by all who were forced into its hands. The Poor Laws were also attacked by the newly-emerging middle classes of Victorian England, whose experience of its workings were not as recipients but as the source of its finance, through taxation (the rates).

176 A Brundage. *The Making of the New Poor Law 1832–1839*. 1978.
177 A Digby. *Pauper Palaces*. 1978. A study of the operation of the Poor Laws in a rural (Norfolk) setting which provides an interesting example of the way in which local and regional studies can be set against general and national ones. See also, I Anstruther. *The Scandal of the Andover Workhouse*. 1973.
178 D Fraser. (Ed). *The New Poor Law in the Nineteenth Century*, 1976. Includes a chapter by Flinn on medical services under the Poor Law.
179 J D Marshall. *The Old Poor Law 1795–1834*. 1968.
180 M E Rose. *The Relief of Poverty 1834–1914*. 1972.

2.6 Population

181 M W Flinn. *British Population Growth 1700–1850*. 1970. A book in the series prepared for the Economic History Society. See also, Taylor (175). Provides a brief introduction to the changes and to the debates surrounding the explanations for the growth of population. See also, Flew (153).
182 R Lawton. (Ed). *The Census and Social Structure: An Interpretative Guide to Nineteenth-Century Censuses for England and Wales*. 1978. Essential reading for any one who will use census data in their project.
183 T McKeown. *The Modern Rise of Population*. 1976. One of the most important and controversial studies of modern population growth. Argues that the growth was due not to changes in medical science, knowledge or practice, but to changes in nutrition. A crucial book for all interested in the contribution made by nursing to the health of the population.
184 R Mitchinson. *British Population Change Since 1860*. 1977. Companion to Flinn (181).
185 C I Pennington. Morality and Medical Care in Eighteenth-Century Glasgow. *Medical History*, 23. 1979. Supports McKeown (183).
186 N Tranter. *Population Since the Industrial Revolution: The Case of England and Wales*. 1973. The best guide to the field. Has a good introduction which covers all the major debates clearly and simply. The tables and statistics are set out in a very accessible form and there is a good bibliography. This book is essential reading for any study of the growth of population and its effects on social policy and social change.

2.7 Public health

Recent studies would suggest that cholera was a major factor in producing new attitudes to state intervention in the health of the nation through public health measures (196; 197). It was perhaps the realisation that cholera was not class-specific in its selection which prompted many contemporaries to argue for state intervention in the conditions under which most of the population lived.

187 A Briggs. Cholera in the Nineteenth Century. *Past and Present*. 19. 1966.

188 C F Brockington. *Public Health in the Nineteenth Century*. 1965. See also his *Short History of Public Health* (2nd edition 1966).
189 C Creighton. *A History of Epidemics in Britain*. 1894. Now reissued with an Introduction and additional material by D E C Eversley, E A Underwood and L Ovenall, 2 volumes. 1965. Remains an essential source for statistical data.
190 M Durey. *The Return of the Plague: British Society and the Cholera 1831–32*. 1979.
191 W M Frazer. *A History of English Public Health 1834–1939*. 1950.
192 R Hodgkinson. (Ed). *Science and Public Health*. Open University. *Science and the Rise of Technology since 1800*. Block V, Unit 10. 1973.
193 D Large and F Round. *Public Health in Mid-Victorian Bristol*. 1974.
194 R A Lewis. *Edwin Chadwick and the Public Health Movement 1832–1854*. 1952.
195 N Longmate. *King Cholera: The Biography of a Disease*. 1966.
196 R J Morris. *Cholera 1832: The Social Response to an Epidemic*. 1976. An example of the new style of medical history, which here attempts to set a disease system within an analysis of the class structures.
197 M Pelling. *Cholera, Fever and English Medicine 1825–1865*. 1978.
198 A Raistrick. *Two Centuries of Industrial Welfare: The London (Quaker) Lead Company 1692–1905*. 1938. Reprinted 1977. See also, Charley (458).
199 P E Razzell. *Edward Jenner's Cowpox Vaccine: The History of a Medical Myth*. 1977. Generally argues that innoculation and not vaccination led to a fall in the death rate from the eighteenth century onwards.
200 H Williams. Public Health and Local History. *Local History*, xiv, 4. 1980. Important contribution to the use of local studies in history.

2.8 Housing

201 H Dyos and M Wolff. (Eds). *The Victorian City*. 1973.
202 E Gauldie. *Cruel Habitations: A History of Working-Class Housing 1780–1918*. 1974.
203 J Melling. (Ed). *Housing, Social Policy and the State*. 1980. Melling's Introduction is a useful survey of the debate over the role of the state in housing and related social policy areas.

204 A S Wohl. Octavia Hill and the Homes of the London Poor. *Journal of British Studies*, 10 (2). 1971.
205 A S Wohl. *The Eternal Slum*. 1977.

2.9 Education and the health care of children

206 A Davin. Imperialism and Motherhood. *History Workshop*, Spring 1978. A very important article which links the role of mother to the needs of an imperial power faced with increasing unrest at home and competition abroad.
207 The Department of Education and Science. *The School Health Service 1908–1974*. 1976.
208 C Dyhouse. *Girls Growing Up in Late Victorian and Edwardian England*. 1981. A study of the ways in which middle- and working-class girls were socialised into specific roles through the system of education.
209 J D Hirst. A Failure 'without parallel': The School Medical Service and London County Council 1907–1912. *Medical History*, 25. 1981. Should be read in conjunction with (207).
210 J Hurt. *Elementary Schooling and the Working Classes*. 1979.
211 J Kamm. *Hope Deferred: Girls Education in English History*. 1965.
212 J Lewis. *The Politics of Motherhood: Child and Maternal Welfare in England 1900–1939*. 1980.
213 G A N Lowndes. *The Silent Social Revolution: An Account of the Expansion of Public Education in England and Wales 1895–1935*. 1950.
214 G F MacCleary. *The Early History of the Infant Welfare Movement*. 1933. Early and uncritical study by one of the leading protagonists.
215 I Pinchbeck and M Hewitt. *Children in English Society*. Issued as two separate volumes in 1969 and 1973.
216 H Silver. *The Concept of Popular Education*. 1965. Has a useful bibliography and discusses women's education.
217 B Simon. (Ed). *Studies in the History of Education*. 1969.

2.10 The Welfare State

The 'Welfare State' is an ambiguous concept, as Titmus (228) has pointed out (p 53) and today we seem to accept that it exists and has done so since 1948. This is the view of Hay (145) who writes that 'The Labour government's social legislation of 1945–8, which it is generally accepted as marking the institution of the welfare state, was the outcome of much of the social planning which had gone on during the second world war.' (pp 3–4) Consequently, the National Health Service and the social services which followed on from the wartime regulations mark the start of that 'indefinable abstraction "The Welfare State"'. (Fraser (220) p 222.) However, it may be that Fraser is correct in his conclusion that the British Welfare State 'was both an end and a beginning . . . [it] was not the product of a spontaneous act of creation in 1948 but the latest stage on a dynamic process of adjustment between individual and society. The British Welfare State was not born—it had evolved.' (p 222)

The books and articles listed here reflect this approach, that the welfare state had its origins in the social policies of the past and its eyes on a future which it was helping to create.

218 R C Birch. *The Shaping of the Welfare State*. 1974.
219 M Bruce. *The Coming of the Welfare State*. 1961.
220 D Fraser. *The Evolution of the British Welfare State*. 1973. An excellent introduction to the subject which has rightly assumed the status of textbook. An interesting mixture of primary and secondary sources from several historical disciplines and an excellent bibliography to publication date. There are some examples of contemporary documents at the end of the book. The general thesis which Fraser pursues is that social policy development was 'an erratic and pragmatic response of government and people to the practical individual and community problems of an industrialised society.' The Welfare State, in Fraser's view, was not created but 'evolved'. (p 1; p 222)

221 B B Gilbert. *The Evolution of National Insurance in Great Britain*. 1966. An overlong but now standard work which is worth dipping into using the index.
222 J R Hay. *The Origins of the Liberal Welfare Reforms 1906–1914*. 1975. Short introduction to the issues; very readable. With a good bibliography.
223 U Henriques. *Before the Welfare State: Social Administration in Early Industrial Britain*. 1979. One of the best introductions to social policy before 1948. Has an excellent bibliography; the book is sub-

divided into manageable chapters which include public health and prisons.
224 E Midwinter. *Social Administration in Lancashire 1830–1860*. 1969.
225 H Pelling. State Intervention and Social Legislation in Great Britain before 1914. *Historical Journal*, 10 (3). 1967. An important and clear review article, reviewing literature to publication date.
226 D Roberts. *Victorian Origins of the British Welfare State*. 1968.
227 J F Sleeman. *The Welfare State: Its Aims, Benefits and Costs*. 1973.
228 R M Titmus. *Essays on 'The Welfare State'*. 1958. Important work by an influential author close to the events he analyses. The nurse historian and even practitioner will be intrigued by his comments on nursing practices and discipline in Chapter 7, where Titmus is concerned with 'organizational fetish'. (p 128)

2.11 The National Health Service

229 B Abel-Smith. *The National Health Service: The First Thirty Years*. 1978.
230 H Eckstein. *The English Health Service: Its Origins, Structures and Achievements*. 1958.
231 R Hodgkinson. *The Origins of the National Health Service*. 1967.
232 J E Pater. *The Making of the National Health Service*. 1981.
233 B Watkin. *The National Health Service: The First Phase 1948–1974 and After*. 1978.

2.12 Charity and philanthropy; social theory

234 W S Churchill. *Liberalism and the Social Problem*. 1909. A 'manifesto' of the 'New Liberalism'; see also Fraser (220), Chapter 7 for a discussion of this development.
235 L T Hobhouse. *Liberalism*. 1911.
236 A M MacBriar. *Fabian Socialism and English Politics 1884–1918*. 1962. A critical assessment of the role of Fabianism in the development of social policy.
237 C E Morgan. Working-Class Women and Social Movements of Nineteenth-Century England. Unpublished PhD thesis, University of Iowa. 1979.

238 C L Mowat. *The Charity Organisation Society 1869–1913*. 1961. The COS was one of the most important non-statutory groups within the area of social policy and intervention in the nineteenth century. It championed the case-study approach to the relief of distress and led the attack on 'indiscriminate' charity. The method of working adopted by COS visitors permeated British social work for decades. Under the banner of self-help and effective relief, the COS paved the way for the means test as indicator of merit for help.
239 F K Prochaska. *Women and Philanthropy in Nineteenth-Century England*. 1980. An important study of the role played by middle class women in the formation of social policy and social control.
240 G B Shaw. *Fabian Essays in Socialism*. 1920. The 1962 edition has a good introduction to this important group, written by Briggs.
241 B Webb. *My Apprenticeship*. 1926 and *Our Partnership*. 1948.
242 A S Wohl. *Endangered Lives: Public Health in Victorian Britain*. 1983. Wide-ranging work which deals with many historical debates in the study of public health. There is a superb bibliography including medical history works. A chapter on state medicine and a discussion on the links between imperialism and children in society offer new insights.

3 RELIGION

The role of religion in social change has a long history as an area of debate. For some, such as Thompson (98), religious belief has 'hindered' the development of working-class radicalism or at least coloured it; other historians have identified a close relationship between religious affiliation and economic change (89). The most relevant aspect of the history of religion to the nursing historian is the role played by the sisterhoods in the care of the sick and the poor. Some of the reading for this will be found in the sub-division dealing with nursing history; here we list those works which examine religion in a wider context.

243 A M Allchin. *The Silent Rebellion: Anglican Religious Communities 1845–1900*. 1958. Examines the background to the Oxford Movement which influenced Nightingale's approach to both religion and to the role to be played by religious orders in nursing.
244 P F Anson. *The Call of the Cloister: Religious Communities and*

Kindred Bodies in the Anglican Community. 1955. Uncritical but useful for listing details of sisterhoods.
245 W R Arnstein. *Protestant versus Catholic in Mid-Victorian England: Mr Newdegate and the Nuns*. 1982.
246 O Chadwick. *The Victorian Church*. 1966. Has a useful bibliography.
247 M A Crowther. *Church Embattled: Religious Controversy in Mid-Victorian England*. 1970.
248 M Hill. *The Religious Order: A Study of Virtuous Religion and Its Legitimation in the Nineteenth-Century Church of England*. 1973. The most useful guide to the relationship between sisterhoods, religion, women and nursing in the nineteenth century. Hill traces the way in which some middle-class women moved out of religious organisations and into secular ones, which included nursing, in response to changing economic and demographic circumstances.
249 K S Inglis. *Churches and the Working-Classes in Victorian England*. 1963.
250 W G Ward. *Religion and Society in England 1790–1850*. 1972.

4 MEDICINE AND THE MEDICAL PROFESSION

The development of nursing has been inextricably linked to that of medicine, not because they 'naturally' form a complimentary and self-obvious caring sector, but rather because of the power wielded by the profession of medicine since the eighteenth century. It is only recently that nurses and historians have attempted to separate that constructed homogeneity, to break down the dominance of medicine and medical science over nursing and nursing care. That new approach owes much to the upsurge of interest in feminist critiques of patriarchy and to a new generation of medical historians.

Until recently, medical history consisted in the main of the lives of the 'great' men of medicine or accounts of the heroic struggle against disease and unenlightenment. This approach—characterised as 'whiggish' and presenting a developmentalist perspective—is coming under considerable attack. In a recent article, Gabbay (290) pointed out how the new history of medicine could take over some of the concerns of the old and translate them to afford a new understanding of the relationships which characterise medicine. He argued that this new approach could also be used in the study of nursing history. A general introduction to the new style of medical history is given in Woodward and Richards (Eds) (295).

An element generally missing from much of the literature on medical history is an account of the recipients of 'care'—the patients. One recent work which attempts to insert this group into medical history is Smith (293), which has a mass of detail about who the patients were and how they experienced medical attention in the nineteenth and early twentieth centuries.

Some of the impetus for the radical change in the concerns within medical history comes from medical sociology and from studies of the North American health systems; the more accessible of that literature is listed here.

4.1 Contemporary

251 F Buckle. *Vital and Economic Statistics of the Hospitals Infirmaries, etc. for England and Wales for 1863*. 1865. An important contemporary work which served as the backdrop to Nightingale's attack on the hospital system. Concerned primarily with mortality rates.
252 H C Burdett. *Hospitals and the State*. 1881. One of the most prolific contemporary writers on medical, nursing and hospital affairs. A committed laissez-faire follower who nevertheless was a pragmatist in matters relating to the care of the sick.
253 H C Burdett. *The Relative Mortality after Amputations*. 1882. Another example of the work of this reformer and of his use of statistical data to enhance his case. Here he is concerned with the introduction of Listerian techniques during and after major surgery. This volume, even with its many faults, is of great historical importance; it failed, however, to impress his contemporaries, perhaps because Burdett was not a doctor.
254 H C Burdett. *Hints in Sickness: Where to go and What to do*. 1883. Whilst originally published as a guide for the middle classes in case of illness, the book is a valuable guide to contemporary hospital provision.
255 'H'. Through the patient's eyes. *Nursing Times*. xvi, 1921. One of

the few personal portraits from the period, although it is very possible that it was, in fact, written by a nurse and one prominent in the pro-Registration movement. Nevertheless, it does demonstrate some of the contemporary anxieties about 'patient care'.
256 A Hake. *Suffering London*. 1892. A damning indictment of the state of health provision for the labouring classes in the capital city. Uses a mass of fairly crude statistical data to argue for a better distribution of hospital provision.
257 The Labour Party. *The Labour Movement and the Hospital Crisis: A Scheme for a Hospital Service*. nd. (c 1922). An early indication of the way in which one of the major political parties was moving towards state and socialised medicine.
258 The Labour Party. *The Organisation of Preventive and Curative Medical Services*. nd.
259 E Lynn Linton. *At Night in Hospital*. 1879. A 'lady' tours the wards of one of the London hospitals.
260 R Quain. (Ed). *A Dictionary of Medicine*. 2 volumes. 1882. Most memorable for the contributions on nursing by Nightingale.
261 C West. *Hospital Organisation with Special Reference to . . . Hospitals for Children*. 1877. Really a practitioner's guide on the setting up and running of a small cottage hospital with beds for sick children. Contains an interesting discussion of what sort of nurses ought to be employed, whether they should be lay or religious, married or single; finally cites Nightingale in support of a lay system.

4.2 Guides and reference works

262 G H Brown. *Lives of the Fellows of the Royal College of Physicians in London 1826–1925*. 1955.
263 S Chaff et al. *Women in Medicine: A Bibliography of Literature on Women Physicians*. 1977.
264 E Clarke. *Modern Methods in the History of Medicine*. 1971. Has chapters on oral evidence, autobiography and literature as sources.
265 V G Plarr. *Lives of the Fellows of the Royal College of Surgeons of England*. 2 volumes. 1930. Lists the lives of the Fellows to publication date, since 1843.
266 S J Rogal. A Checklist of Medical Journals Published in England

during the Seventeenth, Eighteenth and Nineteenth Centuries. *British Studies Monitor*, ix, 3. 1980.
267 Wellcome Historical Medical Library. *Current Work in the History of Medicine: An International Bibliography*. Published since 1954.

4.3 Medical professionalisation

268 P Branca. (Ed). *The Medicine Show: Patients, Physicians and the Perplexities of the Health Revolution in Modern Society*. 1977.
269 J L Brand. *Doctors and the State: The British Medical Profession and Government Action in Public Health 1870–1912*. 1965. Useful for its discussion of the power exercised by competing groups within the medical profession.
270 F F Cartwright. *A Social History of Medicine*. 1977. Brief but useful summary of the main issues to publication date. Very much the 'old style' of medical history.
271 J Donnison. *Midwives and Medical Men*. 1977. Ostensibly an account of the professionalisation of obstetrics, this book is also an attack on patriarchy and the imposition of the medical model on one aspect of human life.
272 M Foucault. *The Birth of the Clinic: An Archaeology of Medical Perception*. 1973. An idiosyncratic but seminal work in the reconstruction of power relationships which exist in the arena of health.
273 E Friedson. *The Profession of Medicine*. 1970. Has a section on the relationship between medical professionalisation and the development of modern nursing.
274 B Haley. *The Healthy Body and Victorian Culture*. 1978. Not precisely concerned with professionalisation, but listed here because it is a case study of the way in which Victorians took to scientific and heroic medicine with a will.
275 F Honigsbaum. *The Division in British Medicine: A History of the Separation of General Practice from Hospital Care 1911–1968*. 1979. Over-emphasises the role of the Socialist Medical Society.
276 J J Keevil. *Medicine and the Navy*. 1957. 4 volumes. Later volumes written by Lloyd and Coulter; 1958, 1961 and 1963.
277 G Millerson. *The Qualifying Associations*. 1964. Listed here because it deals with other groups than doctors and thus is a useful contrast.

278 N and J Parry. *The Rise of the Medical Profession: A Study of Collective Social Mobility*. 1976. Draws on recent writing in the sociology of professions and medical sociology; at times its lack of clarity for the uninitiated detracts from its message.
279 M J Peterson. *The Medical Profession in Mid-Victorian London*. 1978.
280 W J Reader. *Professional Men*. 1966. The classic study of the traditional professions, law, the church and medicine. Easy to read but offers little insight into the ways in which professions create, operate and maintain power relationships.
281 S Reverby and D Rosner. (Eds). *Health Care in America: Essays in Social History*. 1979. An important contribution to the new medical history.
282 M R Walsh. *Doctors Wanted: No Women Need Apply: Sexual Barriers in the Medical Profession 1835–1975*. 1977. Whilst concerned with North America, it is a crucial work in the history of medicine and professionalisation.
283 S and B Webb. *The State and the Doctor*. 1910. Came out of their Minority Report to the Poor Law Commission 1909. Presents a Fabian socialist response to the health needs of the time.
284 J L West. *The Taylors of Lancashire: Bonesetters and Doctors 1750–1890*. 1977. A typical 'family' history—Mr West's wife is the descendant of the subject of the book—and somewhat anecdotal; nevertheless, it provides an important source for a study of the development of professional medicine and for the division of labour within it.
285 G R Williams. *The Age of Miracles: Medicine and Surgery in the Nineteenth Century*. 1981.

4.4 General works

286 S T Anning. *The History of Medicine in Leeds*. 1980. Like most of the other works by this author, totally uncritical.
287 O Checkland and M Land. (Eds). *Health Care as Social History: The Glasgow Case*. 1982. Essential reading for the new history of medicine. Demonstrates the impact of local government, the Poor Law, voluntary agencies and so on, on the health of a local population.
288 S Cherry. The Hospitals and Population Growth: The Voluntary

General Hospitals, Mortality and Local Populations in the English Provinces in the Eighteenth and Nineteenth Centuries. Parts 1 and 2. *Population Studies*, xxxiv, 1 & 2. 1980. Important article, although overlong, which enters the debate about the effect of hospitals and hospital based medicine on changes in population and health care. Clear and helpful tables.
289 J Cule. *A Doctor for the People: 200 Years of General Practice in Britain*. 1980.
290 J Gabbay. Whigs and Stories: Changing Visions in the Histories of Medicine. *Bulletin of the History of Nursing*, 2. Autumn 1983.
291 R Gibson. *The Family Doctor: His Life and History*. 1980.
292 The Hospital Reform Enquiry Committee, Birmingham. *Hospital Reform: Birmingham 1891*. 1891. An example of the way in which a local pressure group utilised statistical data in support of change.
293 F B Smith. *The People's Health 1830–1910*. 1979. First full-length study of the needs of people rather than those of the professionals in the health arena. Divided into chapters based on age groups, with some information on nursing services.
294 C Webster. (Ed). *Health, Medicine and Mortality in the Sixteenth Century*. 1979.
295 J Woodward and D Richards. (Eds). *Health Care and Popular Medicine in Nineteenth-Century England*. 1977. The chapter by the editors is essential reading as an introduction to the critiques of the history of medicine.
296 A J Youngson. *The Scientific Revolution in Victorian Medicine*. 1979.

4.5 Hospitals and hospital planning

297 B Abel-Smith. *The Hospitals 1800–1948: A Study in Social Administration in England and Wales*. 1964. Essential reading, whether in one go or through dipping in. A mine of detail and information. It is concerned not only with the formal hospital network but also with professionalisation among the administrators and nurses.
298 C Andrews. *The Dark Awakening: A History of St Andrew's Hospital, Bodmin*. 1978. The history of a mental hospital.
299 C T Andrews. *The First Cornish Hospital*. 1975.

300 S T Anning and W J K Wallis. *A History of the Leeds School of Medicine: One and a Half Centuries 1831–1981*. 1982.
301 R Bewick. *The History of a Provincial Hospital: Burton upon Trent*. 1974.
302 C Brewer. *A Brief History of the Liverpool Royal Infirmary 1887–1978*. 1980.
303 B Curle. *St Charles Hospital 1881–1981: A Century of Service*. 1981.
304 C W Gibby. *Sherburn Hospital*. 1980.
305 J C Humble and P Hansell. *Westminster Hospital 1716–1974*. 1974.
306 F D Long. *King Edward's Hospital Fund for London 1897–1942*. 1942.
307 I S L Loudon. The Origins and Growth of the Dispensary Movement in England. *Bulletin of the History of Medicine*, 55. 1981. Serves to remind historians of the eighteenth-century origins of many hospitals.
308 The Medical Committee. St Mark's Hospital, London. *The Collected Papers of St Mark's Hospital, London: Centenary Volume 1835–1935*. 1935.
309 N Moore. *A History of St Bartholomew's Hospital*. 1918.
310 G Marson. *St Peter's Hospital for Stone 1860–1960*. 1960.
311 N Pevsner. *A History of Building Types*. 1976. Illustrates the architectural and hence ideological links between hospital design and the design of other buildings including prisons, factories and schools.
312 F N L Poynter. (Ed). *The Evolution of Hospitals in Britain*. 1968. A good starting point with short contributions on various aspects of hospital development. The contribution by Simpson deals with the role of modern nursing in the growth of the hospital system and its effectiveness.
313 G M Smith. *A History of Bristol Royal Infirmary*. 1917.
314 J D Thompson and G Goldin. *The Hospital: A Social and Architectural History*. 1975.
315 F F Waddy. *The History of Northampton General Hospital 1743–1948*. 1974.
316 G Whitcombe. *The Infirmary at Gloucester*. 1903.
317 J Woodward. *To Do The Sick No Harm: A Study of the British Voluntary Hospital System to 1875*. 1974. An important contribution to the debate over the role played by hospitals in reducing mortality rates.

4.6 Psychiatry and psychology; marginal medicine

318 R J Cooter. Phrenology and British Alienists c 1825–1845: Part 1: Converts to Doctrine: Part 2: Doctrine and Practice. *Medical History*, 20. 1976.
319 K Doerner. *Madmen and the Bourgeoisie: A Social History of Insanity and Psychiatry*. 1980.
320 K Jones. *Lunacy, Law and Conscience 1744–1845*. 1955.
321 K Jones. *A History of the Mental Health Services*. 1972.
322 W L Parry Jones. *The Trade in Lunacy: A Study of Private Madhouses in England in the Eighteenth and Nineteenth Centuries*. 1972.
323 P McCandless. 'Build! Build!': The Debate over the Care of the Chronically Insane in England 1850–1870. *Bulletin of the History of Medicine*, 53. 1979.
324 J B Russell. *A History of Witchcraft: Sorcerers, Heretics and Pagans*. 1980. In the wake of the attempts at 'de-professionalising' medicine and the new approaches to medical history, witchcraft and similar 'marginal' practices are being seen as important to the provision of all kinds of services, including health, for many of the pre-industrial population.
325 A T Scull. (Ed). *Madhouses, Mad Doctors and Madmen: The Social History of Psychiatry in the Victorian Era*. 1981.
326 A T Scull. *Museums of Madness: The Social Organisation of Insanity in Nineteenth-Century England*. 1979.
327 G Sutherland and S Sharp. 'The Fust Official Psychologist in the Wurrld': Aspects of the Professionalisation of Psychology in Early Twentieth-Century Britain. *History of Science*, xviii, 3. 1980.
328 A Walk. Gloucester and the Beginnings of the RMPA *Journal of Mental Science*, 107. 1961. An important article for its contribution to the history of psychiatric nursing.

5 WOMEN'S HISTORY

The fact that most nurses are women and that their experiences both as women and as workers has been bound up with contemporary definitions of womanhood, definitions which change over time from, for example, good wife to good mother, appears to have escaped the notice of most historians of nursing. Even the apparent contradictions posed by male nurses have received scant regard, *pace* Gamarnikow (352). This is not altogether surprising when we remember that women have, for centuries, been excluded from written history, except as appendages or as aberrations. The burgeoning women's movement of the 1960s threw down the challenge to conventional history to find a role for women in history. That challenge has, to some extent, gone unheeded or with a mere nod towards the place of women in the labour market (55). Consequently there has developed a body of literature, generally outside the formal structures of history and sociology as discrete disciplines, which concerns itself with the reconstruction of women's roles in society and in social change.

The historian of nursing owes a debt to this new feminist history, if only for the way in which it is helping nurses to distance themselves from the medical profession and its dominating influence over practice and received history. In this sub-division are listed some of the most significant works in this new history, even where they appear of only marginal use to the historian of nursing. Also listed are several bibliographical works which will guide you to specific areas of concern where women's history and nursing history may and ought to coincide. (See, in particular, the bibliographies in Vicinus (360) and (361).)

5.1 Contemporary works

329 C Saleeby. *Woman and Womanhood.* 1909. An influential work by a leading eugenicist in which nurses are portrayed as single women who have (or ought) to come to terms with their 'spinster' status by becoming the 'mothers' of their patients. Florence Nightingale is shown to have been the 'mother' of the Crimean Army.

330 A M Anderson. *Memorandum on Subsidiary Health and Kindred Services for Women.* 1919. A report produced for the Ministry of Reconstruction following the end of the First World War. It attempted to find places for women in the labour market as they were displaced by returning male workers. One way suggested was through emigration to the colonies and Dominions, and there were schemes to encourage women with nurse 'training' to go to Canada.

331 J M F Brownlow. *Women's Work in Local Government.* 1911.

332 Lady S M Jeune. (Ed). *Ladies at Work*. 1893. This interesting guide to work for the 'surplus' women of the late nineteenth century includes papers on teaching and nursing by 'experts'. One of the more important functions of this and other similar works was to portray certain types of employment as 'suitable' for 'ladies', by which was meant women who were no longer supported by their families and who had to compete for work in a labour market dominated by men and women with longer traditions of paid employment. Needless to say, they also served as propaganda for these careers, and many of the recruits were not drawn from this middle rank of society, but from women aspiring to higher economic and social status.
333 Mrs Phillips. (Ed). *Dictionary of Employment Open to Women*. 1898. Published by the Women's Institute and providing a list of 'suitable' work for women in which they might make a career. It provides details of pay and conditions of service for many of the new service sector industries.
334 G Stone. *Women War Workers*. 1917.
335 R Strachey. *Careers and Opportunities for Women*. 1935. Written by a feminist and not particularly complimentary about the contemporary state of nursing.

5.2 Guides and reference works

336 M Evans and D Morgan. *Work on Women: A Guide to the Literature*. 1970.
337 R J Evans. The History of European Women: A Critical Survey of Recent Research. *Journal of Modern History*, lii, 4. 1980.
338 B Freidman. (Ed). *Women's Work and Women's Studies 1973–1974: A Bibliography*. 1975.
339 B Kammer. (Ed). *The Women of England from Anglo-Saxon Times to the Present: Interpretative Bibliographical Essays*. 1980.
340 E O Heelerstein, L P Hume and K M Offen. (Eds). *Victorian Women: A Documentary Account of Women's Lives in Nineteenth-Century England, France and the United States*. 1981.
341 P Hollis. *Women in Public: The Women's Movement 1850–1900*. 1979. A collection of documents by contemporary women which includes positions taken on medicine and nursing by such people as Nightingale, Elizabeth Garrett, Elizabeth Blackwell and Sophia Jex-Blake.

5.3 General works

342 O Banks. *Faces of Feminism: A Study of Feminism as a Social Movement.* 1981. An important new work which assesses the relationship between women's social activities and religion and education. Crucial text for the background to any study of nursing reform or nursing biography.

343 P Branca. *Silent Sisterhood: Middle Class Women in the Victorian Home.* 1975.

344 P Branca. *Women in Europe Since 1750.* 1978. Perhaps too much of an overview and light on primary research; useful for a summary of the 'surplus women' debate which is said to have been a factor in opening up nursing to reform.

345 H Braverman. *Labour and Monopoly Capitalism.* 1974. Listed here for the contribution made by this work to the analysis of the sexual and class division of labour and the notion of skill, particularly as applied to women's work. There is a very good precis of Marx and his approach to labour in capitalist societies.

346 J N Burstyn. *Victorian Education and the Ideal of Womanhood.* 1980. Important critique of the ways in which society conditions women into specific roles, including feminity, gentility and motherhood.

347 L Davidoff. *The Best Circles: Social Etiquette and the Season.* 1973.

348 B Ehrenreich and D English. *Complaints and Disorders: The Sexual Politics of Sickness.* 1973. Short and readable but very important critique of medical power, which is shown as one way in which society subordinated women.

349 B Ehrenreich and D English. *For Her Own Good: 150 Years of the Experts' Advice to Women.* 1978.

350 A J Hammerton. *Emigrant Gentlewomen: Genteel Poverty and Female Emigration 1830–1914.* 1979. Should be read in conjunction with works on the 'surplus women' debate and 330. The first chapter is very helpful as a summary of the major feminist contributions to women's history.

351 P Hilden. Women's History: The Second Wave. *Historical Journal,* 25 (2). 1982. A review article.

352 A Kuhn and A-M Wolpe. (Eds). *Feminism and Materialism:*

Women and Modes of Production. 1978. Includes an article by Gamarnikow on patriarchy and nursing.
353 J Mitchell and A Oakley. (Eds). *The Rights and Wrongs of Women*. 1976. Oakley's contribution on the professionalisation of childbirth is a classic of its kind. See also the contribution by Davidoff on the ideology of the home.
354 W Neff. *Victorian Working Women: An Historical and Literary Study of Women in British Industry and Professions 1832–1850*. 1966.
355 J L Newton, M P Ryan and J R Walkowitz. (Eds). *Sex and Class in Women's History*. 1983.
356 M M Postan. (Ed). *Eileen Power's 'Medieval Women'*. 1975.
357 M Stacey and M Price. Women and Power. *Feminist Review*, 5. 1980.
358 R Strachey. *The Cause: A Short History of the Women's Movement in Great Britain*. 1928. New edition 1978. Of interest for its reassessment of Nightingale's feminism and for its reprinting of her '*Cassandra*'.
359 B Taylor. *Eve and the New Jerusalem*. 1983. A recent attempt to see women as political agents particularly within the labour movement and within socialism.
360 M Vicinus. (Ed). *Suffer and Be Still: Women in the Victorian Age*. 1972. Includes an article on governesses and has an excellent bibliographical essay by Kammer.
361 M Vicinus. (Ed). *A Widening Sphere: Changing Roles of Victorian Women*. 1977. Has part 2 of Kammer's bibliography (360).

5.4 Women and work

362 G Braybon. *Women Workers in the First World War*. 1981. Concentrates mainly on manual and factory labour.
363 S Burman. (Ed). *Fit Work for Women*. 1979. The article by Summers on women and philanthropy in the nineteenth century is a useful introduction to the field.
364 J Cassin-Scott. *Women at War 1939–1945*. 1980.
365 M Ebery and B Preston. *Domestic Service in Late Victorian and Edwardian England 1871–1914*. 1976. Uses computer-assisted analysis of census data to reconstruct the extent of domestic service in the period.
366 S Hogg. The Employment of Women in Great Britain 1891–1921.

Unpublished PhD Thesis. University of Oxford. 1964. Important analysis of the changes and explanations of change in women's work in the period which saw the real growth of nursing. Includes a brief discussion of nursing as women's work and has some very useful tables and other statistical data.
367 L Holcombe. *Victorian Ladies at Work: Middle Class Working Women 1850–1914*. 1973. Useful introduction to the principal 'white-blouse' work opportunities, including nursing, for women in the late Victorian period. Criticised by many for a total lack of understanding of class and its relationship to women as workers.
368 A V John. *By the Sweat of Their Brow: Women Workers at Victorian Coal Mines*. 1980.
369 T McBride. *The Domestic Revolution: The Modernisation of Household Service in England and France 1820–1920*. 1976. Despite its title, has little new data for England.
370 A Marwick. *Women at War 1914–1918*. 1977. An overview of the major economic, political and occupational changes affecting women in the period.
371 C Partington. *Women Teachers in the Twentieth Century in England and Wales*. 1976.
372 I Pinchbeck. *Women Workers and the Industrial Revolution 1750–1850*. 1930.
373 M Phillips and W S Tomkinson. *English Women in Life and Letters: Women in the Professions*. 1927.
374 J Scott and L Tilly. *Women, Work and Family*. 1978. A very good synthesis of the relationships between women's work and family life in Europe.
375 P Taylor. *Women Domestic Servants 1919–1939*. 1976.
376 P Thane. Women and the Poor Law in Victorian and Edwardian England. *History Workshop*, 6. Autumn 1978.
377 A Tropp. *The School Teachers*. 1957.
378 J West. (Ed). *Work, Women and the Labour Market*. 1982. Jackie West has a very readable style and makes very complex issues clear. The book has a good bibliography of material concerned with the sexual division of labour.
379 W B Whitaker. *Victorian and Edwardian Shop Workers*. 1973.
380 F Widdowson. *Going Up Into The Next Class: Women Elementary*

Teacher Training 1840–1914. 1980. An excellent, short and readable study of a comparative occupation to nursing. The pun in the title could be equally applied to nursing and social mobility.

6 NURSING HISTORY

In this sub-division we list the works which are specifically about nursing and its development; the works which are most accessible in the growing body of literature which goes to make up nursing history or the history of nursing. It is important to note, however, that not all would agree that there is such a thing as 'nursing history' or even the history of nursing; Carpenter (391) argues that there ought not to be a separate history of nursing, it is but 'one chapter in the history of labour'. He suggests that to construct a discipline around nursing *per se* is a direct consequence of 'reformed' nursing and may be part of the way in which one group of nurses seek to differentiate themselves from another, including non-'professional' nurses, like the village nurse of the nineteenth century (Carpenter (391) p 125). In studying the development of nursing we must constantly be aware of this debate, and whether we accept it or not, we should endeavour to contribute to it. One way the nursing historian can contribute to the debate is by being explicit about the theoretical position and assumptions which underlie research and publication; we can also come to terms with Carpenter's criticisms if the studies of nursing are contextual, set within specific and identifiable historical periods and debates.

Many old histories of nursing appear to have confused the history of nursing with the ethics of nursing or with past research into nursing practice (393; 395; 439). In general, those authors who seek to justify the study of the history of nursing approach the subject indirectly, usually by a critique of existing literature (for example, 391). The study of the history of nursing has had a longer academic tradition in the United States, in part due to its baccalaureate system of nurse education; in Great Britain, as is shown by some of the works listed here, the study of nursing history has largely been the concern of members of the profession or apologists for it, with a consequent emphasis on the developmental approach which Celia Davies has so succinctly critcised (391).

The sub-division is divided further and somewhat arbitrarily: for example, works by and about Florence Nightingale, other than strictly biographical works, are grouped together. There is a section dealing with nursing textbooks—textbooks of practice, that is—which includes several contemporary guides to nurse training and the prospects of work after qualification. Indeed, if there is one feature which pervades nursing history to date it is the emphasis on the professional or trained nurse, whether generalist, specialist or even community-based. Little work has yet been done on the women displaced by reformed nursing and the new nurses—the village nurses, the wise women or even those accused of witchcraft. Future work in the history of nursing, as is happening in the history of medicine, will need to go beyond the certificate-oriented world and into the everyday world of patients. It is there that the historian is most likely to find understanding of the health care problems and solutions of both pre- and post-industrial Britain. It is by understanding that perspective and that 'landscape' that today's nurses may come to reject the model of practice imposed on the nursing profession by a male-dominated society and a male-dominated medical profession.

6.1 Miscellaneous contemporary works

381 E C Barton. *The History and Progress of Poor Law Nursing*. 1926. An important contemporary account; very 'whiggish' but crucial reading.
382 The Labour Party. *The Labour Party and the Nursing Profession*. 1927. A statement of intent by the Labour Party. (See also, 257 and 258.)
383 E Lückes. *What Will Trained Nurses Gain by Joining The British Nurses Association?* 1889. There is no section here dealing specifically with the 'battle' for registration which lasted nearly 40 years. A general background is given in Abel-Smith (422) and it includes some analysis of the personalities involved. This work by Lückes, one of the influential London matrons, is listed because it summarises some of the feelings about state regulation of nursing and the attitudes of some matrons towards registration. Simply put, opposition to state regulation rested upon the belief of many voluntary hospital matrons that it was the name of the hospital, its prestige based on medical care, which marked a nurse out as good. A nurse's reputation did not depend, therefore, on effectiveness or efficiency or even extent of training, except incidentally.

384 J L De Pledge, The History and Progress of Nursing in Poor Law Infirmaries. *Westminster Review*, 142, 2. 1894.
385 G W Potter. *Ministering Women: The Story of the Royal National Pension Fund for Nurses.* 1891. This is the only account to date of one of the first occupational pension and insurance schemes for any professional group. Whilst somewhat laudatory in tone and intent, it is important for the insights it gives into working conditions of many nurses and the interest shown by the middle classes, including Sir Henry Burdett, in social problems of the period.
386 W J H Whittall. *Pensions for Hospital Officers and Staffs.* 1919. A unique study using statistical data of the conditions of service of workers of all grades in the London hospitals of the period.

6.2 Guides and reference works

387 A Austin. *History of Nursing Source Book.* 1957. Crucial and pioneering American work which has itself become a source in the history of nursing.
388 *Nursing Studies Index.* 4 volumes covering the period 1900–1929, 1930–1949, 1950–1956 and 1957–1959. This is a very valuable general guide to the literature which covers all aspects of nursing as well as its development. The most accessible library which has the Index is the Library of the Royal College of Nursing, London. (See useful addresses, page 107).
389 A M C Thompson. (Ed and Compiler). *Bibliography of Nursing 1859–1960.* 1968. A second volume listing sources from 1961–1970 was published in 1974. The Library of the Royal College of Nursing where the late Miss Thompson was librarian, is continuing the production of the Bibliography.

6.3 Approaches to the writing of nursing history

As we noted, few works in the history of nursing address directly the historiography of nursing; the exceptions are listed here. Most of the styles of nursing history writing are covertly contained in the works listed here.

390 T Christy. *Problem Forum on Historical Research*. 1972.
391 C Davies. (Ed). *Rewriting Nursing History*. 1980. This is a collection of essays on nursing history united, according to the editor, by a general desire to reassess much of the received wisdom which is nursing history. The introductory essay by Davies is valuable for drawing out some of the criticisms of the old style of nursing history and for its critique of Abel-Smith (422). Her other contribution serves to remind historians of the international context of modern nursing and that nursing models did not, in all Western countries, follow the British/Nightingale one. Of the other contributions, that by Maggs offers some insights into the use of primary source data, an element often missing from much nursing history. Foster and Sheppard show where some of the important archive material may be found and give some advice on how to use it. Finally, Kratz sums up from the non-historian practitioner viewpoint, and shows what she feels the history of nursing has to offer the working nurse. The contribution by Carpenter on asylum workers highlights the general hospital-oriented perspective of most nursing history.

The work as a whole was intended to open up a new history of nursing; whether it will succeed will be shown in the future writings of these contributors and others like them.

392 F Davis. (Ed). *The Nursing Profession*. 1966. An introduction to the sociology of the professions and now somewhat dated.
393 M L Fitzpatrick. (Ed). *Historical Studies in Nursing*. 1978. A report of a conference held at Teachers College, Boston, in 1978 on the history of nursing in the United States. There are several papers on the results of research, but the importance of this work lies in its demonstration of the relevance of the history of nursing to today's nurses. Christy repeats her conviction that history is relevant to practitioners and academics alike. There is a list of the major nursing archives in the United States at the end of the volume.
394 B Melosh. *'The Physician's Hand': Work, Culture and Conflict in American Nursing*. 1982. One of the new style nursing histories; sets nursing in the context of labour, gender and class conflict.
395 M E Newton. The Case for Historical Research. *Nursing Research*, 14. 1965.

396 M S Newby. The Problems of Teaching Nursing History. *Nursing Times*, 22/29 November 1979. Provides a neat summary of the major 'histories' of nursing, tracing the links between the styles.
397 M A Nutting and L A Dock. *A History of Nursing*. 4 volumes 1907 and 1912. This mammoth work set the tone for much nursing history for the next 60 years. There is a vast amount of reading behind the authors' synthesis, which is international in perspective. The work suffers in some respects from having been written by protagonists of the new and respectable forms of nursing and may well be viewed as a primary source in its own right today. A critique of this and similar works is given in Newby (396).

6.4 Contemporary guides, textbooks and hospital portraits

398 H Balmé. *A Criticism of Nursing Education*. 1937. Supports student status for trainees.
399 L F Barker. *Changing Conditions in Nursing and the Education of Nurses*. 1930. Published in the year which saw the setting up of the Lancet Inquiry into Nursing (see Baly, 424).
400 H C Burdett. *Burdett's Official Directory of Nurses*. 1898. May now be rightly seen as a primary source; originally published as an attempt to 'register' nurses in the same way as medical men. (Maggs, 435.) The volume, published annually, lists about 5000 names in 1898 and 8000 by 1905—only 20 per cent of those eligible to 'register'. The Directory is invaluable for tracing the careers of many individual nurses, and is useful in any discussion about state regulation and registration.
401 H C Burdett. *The Nursing Profession: How and Where to Train*. 1899. Published as a guide to the major training schools for nurses, the volume drew on information collected by Burdett on his visits to many hospitals.
402 H C Burdett. *How To Succeed As A Trained Nurse*. 1913. A companion guide to (401) for the world of work open to the trained nurse, giving pay and conditions of service for many hospitals as well as some of the specialised areas open to nurses.
403 G B Carter. *A New Deal For Nurses*. 1939. A personal statement made in the light of the deliberations of the Athlone Committee. (See Baly (424).)

404 E J Domville. *A Manual for Hospital Nurses*. 1888.
405 E M Fox. *First Lines in Nursing*. 1914.
406 Guys Hospital. *Guys Hospital: Nursing Guide, Handbook of the Nurse's League and Register of Nurses Trained at Guys*. 1904. Used in conjunction with (400) provides a broader data base for a study of recruitment and mobility.
407 E Haldane. *Nursing as a Profession*. 1922. Really a history of nursing through the ages but is of interest for its description of British nursing during the First World War.
408 I A Hampton. (Ed). *Nursing of the Sick*. 1893. (1949 reprint). The Report of a nursing conference held during the World Fair in the United States. Drew together international nursing leaders including Mrs Bedford Fenwick. Important because it shows how the American system of nursing deliberately set out to avoid many of the English problems, in particular over registration and training. See Davies (391).
409 E Lückes. *Hospital Sisters and Their Duties*. 1886.
410 E Lückes. *General Nursing*. 1898. A manual for nurses based on her lectures to trainees at the London Hospital.
411 E McManus. *Hospital Administration for Women*. 1934. A guide mainly for assistant, deputy and the matron grades.
412 E Morley. (Ed). *Women's Work in Seven Professions*. 1914. Contains a chapter by Musson on nursing.
413 H Morten. *How to Become a Nurse*. 1895.
414 H Morten. *From a Nurse's Notebook*. 1899.
415 A Munroe. *The Science and Art of Nursing the Sick*. 1873. An early example of a textbook for nurses under the reformed system, written by a doctor.
416 *The Science and Art of Nursing*. 1908. 4 volumes. Volume 1 contains a history of nursing by Tooley and contributions by nurses and doctors on training, administration and law in nursing. The remainder of the volumes are mimics of medical anatomy and physiology textbooks.
417 I Stewart. Nursing at St Bartholomew's Hospital. *Murray's Magazine*, August 1890. A description of conditions at a leading London voluntary hospital. Formed part of the evidence to the Select Committee on the Metropolitan Hospitals. 1890–1.
418 M Vivian. *Lectures to Nurses in Training*. 1920.
419 M Voysey. *Nursing: Hints to Probationers on Practical Work*. 1901.

A good example of the early manuals for nurses written by a nurse; contains much advice on 'ethics' and morals.
420 J K Watson. *A Handbook for Nurses.* 1899. One of the most successful—in terms of numbers published and reprints—of all such manuals. Written by a doctor and full of intricate details about sanitation, hygiene and ventilation.
421 V Young. *Outlines of Nursing.* 1914.

6.5 General histories of nursing

422 B Abel-Smith. *A History of the Nursing Profession.* 1960. Written by a non-nurse and coming out of his major study of the hospital system (297), this volume has assumed the status of a textbook. Unfortunately, it has also become known as '*the* history' of nursing, despite the author's warning to the contrary. It is of particular importance when dealing with the national politics and power relationships which influenced nursing, although the early period is slightly weak in comparison to the post-1920s.

There is a good guide to the major personalities involved, especially in the registration debates and a critical study of the system of entry to the profession. One major fault which the book has is the lack of a bibliography and a somewhat cavalier attitude to primary source data. However, it remains a classic study of its kind.

423 P Allen and M Jolley. *Nursing, Midwifery and Health Visiting Since 1900.* 1982. Poor scholarship and little to recommend it to historians.
424 M Baly. *Nursing and Social Change.* 1973. Revised and reprinted 1980. This volume demonstrates why nursing history has been periodically published; in this case, it was because the Diploma in Nursing (University of London) course required a study of the development of nursing. The volume, by one of the course tutors, was a result. Originally criticised for relying too heavily on secondary sources, it was, nevertheless, a good guide to the numerous reports and commissions set up to deal with nursing affairs. The two editions also demonstrate the new perspectives in nursing history, with the second including more primary data and less personal observation and more in keeping with its lofty aim of setting nursing within its changing social contexts.

425 V L and B Bullough. *The Care of the Sick: the Emergence of Modern Nursing*. 1979. Apart from a long and useful bibliography this work offers little that is new.
426 L D Dietz. *History and Modern Nursing*. 1963.
427 L L Dock and I Stewart. *A Short History of Nursing*. 1920. See Newby (396).
428 J A Dolan. *Nursing in Society: A Historical Perspective*. 1973.
429 B Ehrenreich and D English. *Witches, Midwives and Nurses: A History of Women Healers*. 1973. More of a polemic than an empirical study; important for drawing attention to the relationships between nursing and women.
430 C Frank. *The Historical Development of Nursing*. 1953. Written by a member of a religious order.
431 J E Gordon. Nurses and Nursing in Britain: Parts 1–23. *Midwife and Health Visitor*. 1970–73. Despite attempting to situate modern nursing to ancient times, this series of articles is very useful because it is nurse-oriented.
432 G J Griffin and H J K Griffin. *History and Trends of Professional Nursing*. 1943.
433 E Jamieson and M Sewall. *Trends in Nursing History*. 1940.
434 P and B Kalish. *The Advance of American Nursing*. 1978. Retains the developmental approach but has important differences, notably the wide range of sources used, including film. Has an excellent bibliography.
435 C Maggs. *The Origins of General Nursing*. 1982. A study very much in the Abel-Smith mould (422), although addressing issues largely ignored by that work. Emphasis is on experiences of nursing, in particular those of the rank and file nurse. Offers some guide to sources in the history of nursing, especially the potential of oral evidence (see 481) and popular literature. The chapter on recruitment is probably one of its strengths and suggests that received wisdom about recruitment needs clarification. Has a useful and wide-ranging bibliography as well as an Appendix dealing with women's work in the period 1880–1914.
436 A E Pavey. *The Story of the Growth of Nursing*. 1959.
437 L R Seymer. *A General History of Nursing*. 1957. Typical example of the old style nursing history—a mega-historical approach with few insights into the processes of change.
438 R H Shryock. *The History of Nursing: An Interpretation of Social*

and Medical Factors. 1959. Like most mega-histories full of generalisations and uncritical assumptions. However, until the advent of 434, perhaps the best example of American nursing history.
439 E B Suhrie, E M Jamieson and M F Sewall. *Trends in Nursing History: Their Social, International and Ethical Relationships*. 1940.
440 S A Tooley. *The History of Nursing in the British Empire*. 1906. Claimed to be the first historian of British nursing (see 416). It is very descriptive and uncritical but consistent with the age in which it was written—the defence of the Empire and the failing fortunes of the British economic, political and social systems. Was not well received by contemporaries and today reads like a guide to work opportunities. An important landmark in the historiography of nursing.
441 R White. *Social Change and the Development of the Nursing Profession: A Study of Poor Law Nursing Service 1848–1948*. 1978. Apart from Barton (381) and De Pledge (384), the Poor Law nursing service has been a closed book to modern readers. The Webbs had drawn attention to the different systems of nursing in their Minority Report (1909) and Abel-Smith devotes a chapter to the Poor Law nurse in his work (422). However, between Barton—who was personally involved with the Poor Law—and White, no writer had looked at the mass of data for that sector, perhaps hiding behind the aphorism that the poor left no records. This is now acknowledged to be untrue; data are available if searched for and we no longer have to rely on the impressions of middle class observers and reformers in order to understand that past. White has, therefore, provided a timely reminder that nursing was not only about the voluntary hospitals and about general nursing; it was also about the care of the chronically sick and the insane. Drawing upon numerous reports, White has woven a picture of the way in which the nursing service within the Poor Law developed and, in particular, the way in which, despite its role as the major provider of care to the mass of the population, it nevertheless became the 'cinderella' service, underfunded, lacking in prestige and ignored by the elite of the profession.

The study has its drawbacks, however; it relies on one type of evidence—that of official reports and the perspective of the civil servant or the reformer. This 'blue book' approach needs to be constantly challenged by other sources. For example, in the later period the details given in the published reports might be enhanced by interviews with some of those involved in producing the reports and involved in policy. Nursing history lacks this balance of evidence and lacks a critical approach based on varieties of evidence. It is to be hoped that White's work will stimulate others to break down her mega-history in order to reconstruct it anew.

6.6 Nursing in specific hospitals and as seen in personal memoirs

442 W Brockbank. *The History of Nursing at the Manchester Royal Infirmary 1752–1929.* 1970. This uncritical and non-contextual study is useful because it reproduces primary data directly.
443 H C Burdett. *Nurse's Food, Work and Recreation.* 1890. Reprinted from his evidence to the Select Committee on the Metropolitan Hospitals 1890/1. A statistical analysis of the conditions of service for many nurses working in the London voluntary hospitals which destroys the comfortable myths much used by reformers.
444 Sir Z Cope. *One Hundred Years of Nursing at St Mary's Paddington.* 1955.
445 M Dickens. *One Pair of Feet.* 1956. A personal account of a nurse's early career. Humorous and perhaps should be treated more as fiction.
446 S W F Holloway. The All Saints Sisterhood at University College Hospital 1862–1899. *Medical History*, 3. 1959.
447 H C O'Neill and E A Barnett. *Our Nurses and the Work They Have to Do.* 1888. An early criticism of conditions of employment for nurses.
448 A Terton. *Lights and Shadows in a Hospital.* 1902.
449 E Wilson. *Gone with the Raj.* 1974. Useful for a discussion of careers and choice in nursing.

6.7 Nursing in mental hospitals

450 F R Adams. From Association to Union: Professional Organisation of Asylum Attendants 1869–1919. *British Journal of Sociology*, xx, 1. March 1969.
451 M Carpenter. *All for One.* 1980. Brief history of the antecedents of the Confederation of Health Service Employees.
452 *In the Mental Hospital: Articles Reprinted from the 'Lancet'.* 1955. Articles on conditions in the mental hospitals before 1921. See, in

particular, the contribution by Hunter, The Rise and Fall of Mental Nursing. See also Carpenter in Davies (Ed), (391).
453 E H Santos and E Stainbrook. A History of Psychiatric Nursing in the Nineteenth Century. *Journal of the History of Medicine and Allied Sciences*, 4. 1949.
454 A Walk. The History of Mental Nursing. *Journal of Mental Science*, 107. January 1961.

6.8 Nursing specialisms

455 M Baly. The Sick Paupers of Bath 1760–1840. *Bulletin of the History of Nursing*, 1. Spring 1983.
456 C C van Blarcom. *The Midwife in England: Being a Study in England of the Working of the English Midwives Act 1902*. 1913.
457 R Browne and R Stones. *The Male Nurse*. 1973. Not really an historical study but it is the only work dealing specifically with this group of nurses.
458 I H Charley. *The Birth of Industrial Nursing: Its History and Development in Great Britain*. 1954. Reissued 1978.
459 R W J Dingwall, Collectivism, Regionalism and Feminism in Health Visiting and British Social Policy. *Journal of Social Policy*, 6. 1978.
460 W C Dowling. Health Visiting. *Health Visitor*, 46. October–December 1973.
461 M F Gill. *District Nursing in Brighton 1877–1974*. 1978.
462 G Hardy. *William Rathbone and the Early History of District Nursing*. 1981. Very antiquarian approach to history; real value lies in pointing out to others how not to do local history. Despite a bold claim in the Introduction to be challenging accepted views of the history of district nursing—notably the role of Nightingale—the book fails to live up to this. See review in *Bulletin of the History of Nursing*, 2. Autumn 1983.
463 M S Newby, The Victorian Origins of Children's Hospital Nursing. *Bulletin of the History of Nursing*, 1. Spring 1983.
464 E Platte. *The Story of the Ranyard Mission 1857–1937*. 1937.
465 M Stocks. *A Hundred Years of District Nursing*. 1960. A readable book most useful for its chronology of events rather than for its analysis.

6.9 Nursing organisations

Most, if not all, studies of nursing organisations are factual summaries of records produced by those organisations. Despite the effort required to plough through such sources, the end results, the published works, seldom seem to justify the time and effort of the authors.

466 E R D Bendall and E Raybould. *A History of the General Nursing Council for England and Wales 1919–1969*. 1969.
467 G Bowman. *The Lamp and the Book: The Story of the Royal College of Nursing 1916–1966*. 1967. Beware of history as a 'story'; very uncritical account which relies heavily on Abel-Smith (422).
468 D C Bridges. *A History of the International Council of Nurses 1899–1964: The First 65 Years*. 1967.
469 B Cowell and D Wainwright. *Behind the Blue Door: The History of the Royal College of Midwives 1881–1981*. 1981.
470 H M Simpson. *The Royal College of Nursing 1916–1976: Role and Action in a Changing Health Service*. 1976.
471 E Wilkie. *The History of the Council for the Education and Training of Health Visitors*. 1979. Useful for recent events (1962–1975), thin on pre-1962 developments. No analysis.

6.10 War and nursing

472 T Bowser. *The Story of British VAD Work in the Great War*. 1917. Produced as part of the war propaganda.
473 E S Haldane. *British Nurse in Peace and War*. 1923.
474 L MacDonald. *The Roses of No Man's Land*. 1980. Attempts to be the definitive history of the VADs. A journalistic approach—extracts from survivors originally appeared on radio—and without the expected critical and corroborative approach of the historian.
475 D G Murray. *They Did Not Pass By*. 1956.
476 J Piggott. *Queen Alexandra's Royal Army Nursing Corps*. 1975. One in a series of 'famous regiments' histories.
477 C Singer. An Eighteenth-Century Naval Ship to Accommodate Women Nurses. *Medical History*, 4. 1960. Fascinating study of an eighteenth-century nursing system; demonstrates what insights may be forthcoming by diligent research and analysis.

6.11 Miscellaneous

478 J Hannam. Leeds Women's Labour League and Women's Health. *Bulletin of the History of Nursing*, 1. Spring 1983. Shows how a pressure group attempted to influence medical care and in particular male attitudes to female disorders.
479 C Jackson. The Archive Collection at the Royal College of Nursing. *Bulletin of the History of Nursing*, 2. Autumn 1983. A discussion of the collections held and recently catalogued by the College.
480 F Jarman. The Development of Conceptions of Nursing Professionalism among General Hospital Nurses 1860–1895. Unpublished MA Thesis, University of Warwick. 1980. Useful for its study of the role of textbooks and manuals for nurses in the production of common values.
481 C Maggs. Oral History and Nursing History. *Nursing Times*, 27, vol. 79. October 1983. Provides a guide to the use of oral evidence in nursing history; has a short bibliography to the subject and some suggestions about possible topics.
482 G Mercer. *The Employment of Nurses: Nursing Labour Turnover in the National Health Service.* 1979. A study of modern 'wastage' and mobility patterns among nurses; should be used as an aid for any discussion of recruitment to nursing.
483 F Walsh. The Historical Collection of the Library of Nursing, Royal College of Nursing. *Bulletin of the History of Nursing*, 2. Autumn 1983.

6.12 Florence Nightingale and nursing

No discussion of nursing can afford to ignore either the writings of Florence Nightingale or the growing mass of literature about her. A study of the bibliography of Nightingale would encapsulate much of the change which has taken place within the study and writing of nursing history in general in recent years. That development has gone from a celebratory hagiography to a rejection of her importance and finally back to a studied reflection of the ways in which she attempted to intervene in nursing affairs. Two recent works point out some of these styles and should be read for an introduction to 'Nightingale-ism'; the works are Smith (571) and Newby (491).

Listed in this section are works which illuminate aspects of Nightingale's involvement in nursing or with reassessments of her relationship with nursing. Studies of her life are not listed here.

484 E R Barritt. Florence Nightingale's Values and Modern Nursing Education. *Nursing Forum*, 12, 1. 1973. An American attempt to reassess Nightingale's religious convictions and their relationship to the development of nurse education in the United States.
485 R Berkley. *The Lady With the Lamp*. 1929. One of the earliest 'serious' stage plays which emphasised the 'heroine of the East' role and set the pattern for most later theatrical descriptions.
486 J Davis. *Florence Nightingale or the Heroine of the East*. 1856. A long and turgid prose-poem in the heroic genre saluting Nightingale's success in the Crimea.
487 F Gavin. *Florence Nightingale: A Lecture*. 1859. Hagiography.
488 F MacDonnell. *Miss Nightingale's Young Ladies: The Story of Lucy Osburn and Sydney Hospital*. 1970. Traditional history of a 'Nightingale', this time in Australia.
489 R Nash. (Ed). *Florence Nightingale to Her Nurses*. 1914. Very useful for primary material by Nightingale on training, education and values. In one extract, Nightingale appeals to her audience of trainees at St Thomas's to recruit their friends to nursing.
490 M S Newby. Florence Nightingale: A Woman of All Time: Myths and Stereotypes. *Bulletin of the Social History of Medicine*, 18. 1976. A brief study of the way in which Nightingale has been used in different contexts to justify often opposing claims and ambitions.
491 F Nightingale. *Notes on Nursing*. 1859.
492 G Pickering. *Creative Malady*. 1974. An attempt to 'explain' Nightingale and others in terms of questionable psychological theory.
493 C Rosenberg. (Ed). *Healing and History*. 1979. An important collection of articles in the new style of medical history. Most useful for Nightingale-ism is Rosenberg's reassessment of her understanding of medical science and her opposition to the germ theory.
494 L R Seymer. *Selected Writings of Florence Nightingale*. 1954.
495 L R Seymer. *Florence Nightingale's Nurses: The Nightingale Training School 1860–1960*. 1960. Seymer tends to over-state the case for the role of Mrs Wardroper.

7 BIOGRAPHY AND AUTOBIOGRAPHY

The study of history is replete with the lives of the great and the significant; indeed, until quite recently, history consisted only of such matters, at least in its academic and published form. Biography can afford the reader or researcher with insights into specific episodes in historically important eras. For example, Blake's biography of Disraeli—R Blake, *Disraeli*, 1966—is vital for any understanding of the development of social policy by his type of toryism in the nineteenth century. Since many biographies are designed for a general and non-specialised audience, they are usually easy to read. If such works also include a full account of the context of the subject, then biography is a very valuable way of helping us understand the past.

Unfortunately, much biography is hagiography—that is, it is uncritical and downright biased in favour of the subject. The 'skeletons' are missing, or else presented in a one-sided manner. This may be because of censorship by the subject or the family or the trustees of the data; it may be the result of the unconscious wish of the author to present the subject in the most favourable light, a typical fault of the acolyte. Single subject biography may also be criticised for choosing atypical personalities for study—although this may be the reason for the study in the first place. Multiple biography (for example 547) suffers from a too simplistic or deterministic model into which several individuals must be squeezed. Finally, although not exhaustively, it should be remembered that many biographies are produced to celebrate an anniversary or to continue a tradition of biographical studies; some are produced as moral tales for others, including children, whilst many nursing biographies appear to be aimed at easing the lot of the new, and perhaps hesitant, recruit to the profession.

7.1 Essays in criticism

496 J Clive. More or Less Eminent Victorians. *Victorian Studies*, 2. 1958. A review of Woodham Smith (576).
497 A O J Cockshut. *Truth to Life: The Art of Biography in the Nineteenth Century*. 1974. The first two chapters deal with the problems

inherent in the use of this source; the remainder of the book is concerned with 'important' nineteenth-century individuals.
498 A Fleishman. *Figures of Autobiography: The Language of Self-Writing in Victorian and Modern England.* 1983.
499 R Gittings. *The Art of Biography.* 1978.
500 W H Greenleaf. Biography and the 'Amateur' Historian: Mrs Woodham Smith's 'Florence Nightingale'. *Victorian Studies*, 3. 1959. Essential review article which effectively destroys Woodham Smith's biography as hagiography.
501 P M Kendall. *The Art of Biography.* 1971.
502 W Mathews. *British Autobiographies: Bibliography of British Autobiographies Published or Written before 1951.* 1955. By no means definitive but a good starting point for information.
503 J Olney. *Metaphors of Self: The Meaning of Autobiography.* 1972.
504 J Olney. (Ed). *Autobiography: Essays Theoretical and Critical.* 1980.
505 R Pascal. *Design and Truth in Autobiography. 1960.*
506 W Shumaker. *English Autobiography: Its Emergence, Material and Form.* 1954.
507 D Vincent. *Bread, Knowledge and Freedom: A Study of Nineteenth-Century Working Class Autobiography.* 1981. An excellent introduction and example of the way in which historians can use autobiography to extend the analysis of social change. Has a good bibliography and is very readable.

7.2 Autobiographies by nurses and patients

508 L Andrews. *No Time for Romance.* 1977. The story of a VAD who went to train at St Thomas's, London, before the end of the Second World War.
509 B Aronovitch. *Give It Time: An Experience of Hospital 1928–1932.* 1974. Harrowing account by a long-stay patient of her experiences in a variety of hospitals—council, voluntary and Poor Law. Brings home the well-known point that the chronic sick were an unwelcome group in the voluntary sector, but were equally a source of immense resource pressures within the State administered sectors. Should be read in conjunction with Robb (563).

510 Sister C Black. *King's Nurse.* 1939. Most famous as nurse to King George V at his death.
511 Lady A Blackwood. *Narrative of Personal Experiences.* 1881. The wife of an army surgeon at Scutari: views on Nightingale, the soldiers and their wives.
512 M E Broadley. *Patients Come First: Nursing at The London Between the World Wars.* 1980.
513 F F Brook. *Nursing in Many Fields.* 1978. A very useful study of one nurse's career pattern and the possible explanations for it. From initial training in Reading, through nursing in the prison service to health visiting in West Yorkshire.
514 B B Carter. *Old Nurse.* 1936. Really the story of a children's nurse/nanny.
515 E Davis. *Autobiography.* 1857. Varied life with experience in the Crimea.
516 M Eagar. *Six Years.* 1906. Nurse to royal children in Russia.
517 F Gilpin. (Ed). *Scenes from Hospital Life.* nd.
518 J Grant. *Come Hither, Nurse.* 1957. A comedy.
519 G M Hardy. *Yes, Matron.* 1951.
520 C M Harker with J Glattbach. *Call Me Matron.* 1980.
521 J Holmes. *The Private Nurse.* 1899.
522 'A Hospital Nurse'. *Memoirs.* 1910.
523 A G Hunt. *Reminiscences.* 1935. Reprinted in 1938 as *This Is My Life.* Particularly useful for a study of orthopaedic nursing.
524 E C Laurence. *A Nurse's Life in War and Peace.* 1912. A strong imperialist theme runs throughout the book.
525 M Lethbridge. *Fortune Grass.* 1934. Together with *Against The Tide.* 1936. Presents the seamier side of London in the early twentieth century.
526 J Lock. *Reluctant Nightingale.* 1970. Went from nursing to become a policewoman.
527 E Locke. *Post-War Letters of a VAD Nurse.* 1933.
528 B McBryde. *A Nurse's War.* 1979.
529 E MacManus. *Matron of Guy's.* 1956. Se ılso 411.
530 J Markham. *The Lamp Was Dimmed: The Story of a Nurse's Training.* 1975.
531 M Powell. *Patients are People: My Life and Work.* 1975.

532 E Prentis. *A Nurse in Time.* 1977. First in a series of pocket sketches.
533 M Ross. *Memoirs of a Private Nurse.* 1929.
534 'A Sister'. *Life in Hospital.* 1884. Mainly a religious tract and an account of how to convert patients away from alcohol and towards religion.
535 M Smith. *Different Drummer.* 1932.
536 A Smithson. *Myself and Others.* 1945. Worked as a nurse in London and Scotland; later became a novelist.
537 M Stannard. *Memoirs of a Professional Lady Nurse.* 1873. A very involved life including nursing, the Californian Gold Rush, murder and a return to nursing.
538 A H Stoney. *In the Days of Queen Victoria: Memoirs of a Hospital Life.* 1910. Reissued 1931. Written by one of the many converts to eugenicist thinking among the newer professionals. The book is a catalogue of social problems among the lower orders and the ways in which the author thought they should be remedied.
539 J Vaizey. *Scenes From Institutional Life.* 1959. Ranks alongside Aronovitch (509) for the insights it affords into the real world of the patient. Vaizey believes that 'institutions give inadequate people what they want—power', a warning to all who work with those who are forced into a dependent role.

7.3 Biography

540 G Battiscombe. *Shaftesbury: A Biography of the Seventh Earl 1801–1885.* 1974. Education, social investigation and welfare.
541 E M Bell. *Octavia Hill: A Biography.* 1942. Housing and middle class philanthropy.
542 G F A Best. *Shaftesbury.* 1964.
543 A Bishop and T Smart. (Eds). *Vera Brittain's War Diary 1913–1917: Chronicle of Youth.* 1981. Useful for her experiences as a VAD nurse.
544 W J Bishop and S Goldie. *A Bio-Bibliography of Florence Nightingale.* 1962. Refers to all Nightingale's printed works and to works about her to publication date. Clearly set out.
545 A E Clark-Kennedy. *Edith Cavell.* 1965.

546 E Cook. *The Life of Florence Nightingale.* 1913. The 'official' biographer of Nightingale but a very thorough study and heavily used by many later studies.
547 Z Cope. *Six Disciples of Florence Nightingale.* 1961. Includes short pieces on Agnes Jones, Lucy Osburn (see 488) and Rebecca Strong.
548 J M Eyler. *Victorian Social Medicine: The Ideas and Methods of William Farr.* 1979.
549 S E Finer. *The Life and Times of Edwin Chadwick.* 1952. Classic biography of a man involved in the Poor Law and public health movements in the first half of the nineteenth century.
550 G B A M Finlayson. *The Seventh Earl of Shaftesbury 1801–1885.* 1981. It is virtually impossible to understand Victorian social policy and thought without reference to Shaftesbury.
551 J Harris. *William Beveridge: A Biography.* 1977. Well written and critical; provides an assessment of one of the most important twentieth-century social policy makers. Contributes to the MacDonagh debate (see 170).
552 W Hector. *The Work of Mrs Bedford Fenwick and the Rise of Professional Nursing.* 1973. More of a chronology than a biography but based on original research. A good study of this important nursing figure remains to be done.
553 E Huxley. *Florence Nightingale.* 1975. 'Coffee-table' book.
554 J Johnson. *Noble Women of Our Time.* 1882. Brief sketches of, among others, Sister Dora, Mary Carpenter and Agnes Jones.
555 R J Lambert. *Sir John Simon 1816–1904 and English Social Administration.* 1963. Illustrates the range of ability and involvement of this central figure in nineteenth-century social policy.
556 S L Levy. *Nassua Senior: Critical Essayist, Classical Economist and Advisor to Governments.* Revised edition 1970.
557 R A Lewis. *Edwin Chadwick and the Public Health Movement 1832–1854.* 1952. A narrower focus than Finer (549).
558 E Longford. *Eminent Victorian Women.* 1980.
559 M Lonsdale. *Sister Dora: A Biography.* 1881. Extreme hagiography.
560 J Manton. *Sister Dora: The Life of Dorothy Pattison.* 1971. A vast improvement in the art of biography compared with Lonsdale (559).
561 E Rathbone. *William Rathbone: A Memoir.* 1905. See also Hardy

(462). A biography by one of the family may not produce the best results.
562 R G Richardson. (Ed). *Nurse Sarah Anne: With Florence Nightingale at Scutari.* 1977.
563 B Robb. (Presenter). *Sans Everything: A Case to Answer.* Not a history or a biography, and yet it is, in one sense, the biography of a sector of the nursing profession. The work presents damning evidence of malpractice, maltreatment and maladministration in the care of the elderly.
564 J Rose. *The Perfect Gentlemen: The Remarkable Life of Dr James Miranda Barry.* 1977. Journalistic but useful for the description of the clashes between Nightingale and the doctors in the Crimea.
565 J Rose. *Elizabeth Fry: A Biography.* 1980. Adds little to the existing literature but serves to remind us that Nightingale was not the first to see a need for change in nursing and the hospital system.
566 R Ryder. *Edith Cavell.* 1975.
567 L R Seymer. *Dame Alicia Lloyd-Still: A Memoir.* 1953.
568 E Showalter. Florence Nightingale's Feminist Complaint: Work, Religion and 'Suggestions for Thought'. *Signs*, vi, 3. 1981.
569 T S and M B Simey. *Charles Booth: Social Scientist.* 1960.
570 F Smith. *The Life and Work of Sir James Kay-Shuttleworth.* 1923. Particularly relevant for an account of the involvement of this Victorian in education and other matters to do with the welfare of the working classes.
571 F B Smith. *Florence Nightingale: Reputation and Power.* 1982. An important contribution to the subject and an overdue corrective to Woodham Smith (576). Not really a biography, rather a study in the analysis of a personality. Contains a very useful listing of all the major Nightingale papers and an up-to-date bibliography.
572 L Strachey. *Eminent Victorians.* 1918. Includes a chapter on Nightingale in what was seen to be a new style of biography. Much abused for his presentation of Nightingale which was not in the eulogistic fashion then popular.
573 S A Tooley. *The Life of Florence Nightingale.* 1904.
574 R K Webb. *Harriet Martineau: A Radical Victorian.* 1960. A Unitarian and an apologist for Nightingale.
575 T J Williams. *Priscilla Lydia Sellon.* 1950. Important for the background to the Sellonite contribution to nursing in the Crimea, and

for the importance of cholera as a factor in producing demands for reform in nursing.

576 C Woodham-Smith. *Florence Nightingale.* 1950. Used primary sources but uncritically. Has been shown to have radically misinterpreted events and motives (see Smith, 571). This work demonstrates the need which exists to identify themes for biographical study before attempting the entire life of an individual.

8 NOVELS AND FICTION

Few historians make conscious use of works of fiction in their writing; those that do tend to refer to classical literature, such as Shakespeare or Conrad. There are some historians and social scientists who have made use of fiction for historical studies, for example Neff (354), Cazamain (580) and Basch (577). What appears to worry historians about fiction as evidence is that fiction is imagination, a creation of a writer's mind and not a mirror of real events. But fiction cannot be produced in a vacuum; the writer is very much an historical figure, part of the events and concerns in which he lives. Thus, it is possible to argue that fiction illustrates contemporary attitudes, concerns, anxieties and hopes, even where the fiction is set in some other age or society, or even in some far-flung utopia. If fiction is used in this way, it can provide valuable evidence of what may be called experiential history. By using novels about nurses and nursing systems, women and medicine, the changing attitudes of specific periods about these developments can be traced, including the advent of reformed nursing. For a discussion of the use of fiction in nursing history, see Maggs (435).

8.1 The use of fiction for historical study

577 F Basch. *Relative Creatures: Victorian Women in Society and the Novel 1837–1867.* 1974. One reason for using fiction as a source in history is that some groups are generally missing from other sources; this is the case with women, particularly in certain periods. Basch mixes fiction and other data to present an important study of women in the nineteenth century which argues that fiction and culture were enlisted by men to subordinate women. The work includes some observations on the influence of Nightingale on nursing.

578 M F Brightfield. The Medical Profession in Early Victorian England as Depicted in the Novels of the Period 1840–1870. *Bulletin of the History of Medicine*, 35 (3). 1961. Perhaps the world authority, until his death, on novels of the medical profession. Includes some minor novels dealing with nurses. Is a short introduction to his full-length study (579) which was thought too cumbersome to publish.
579 M F Brightfield. *Victorian England in its Novels. 1840–1870.* 4 volumes. 1968. Massive collection with extracts of many minor novels covering all aspects of early Victorian life, including medicine and industrialisation. Published after his death in typescript form because the Library of the University of California at Los Angeles felt unable to edit or revise in book form. Not yet improved upon, although provides little analysis.
580 L Cazamain. *The Social Novel in England 1830–1850: Dickens, Mrs Gaskell, Kingsley*. 1903. Reprinted 1973. A social history drawing on fiction from the great names of Victorian culture.
581 L James. *Fiction for the Working Man 1830–1850: A Study of the Literature Produced for the Working Classes in Early Victorian Urban England*. 1963.
582 L James. (Ed). *Print and the People 1819–1851*. 1976.
583 L Leneman. History as Fiction. *History Today*, xxx, 1980.
584 J Louis. The Rational Amusement: Minor Fiction and Victorian Studies. *Victorian Studies*, 14. 1970. Questions the reality of the picture portrayed by Brightfield.
585 L and E Richter. Nurses in Fiction. *American Journal of Nursing*. July 1974. Two practitioners worried by the images of nursing in popular fiction; they argue that nurses should write their own novels.
586 J Rockwell. *Fact in Fiction: The Use of Literature in the Systematic Study of Society*. 1974. Excellent account of the theoretical problems of the use of fiction.
587 M Sadlier. *Nineteenth-Century Fiction: A Bibliographical Record Based on His Own Collection*. 2 volumes. 1951. Reprinted 1969.
588 L Stevenson. (Ed). *Victorian Fiction: A Guide to Research*. 1966.

8.2 Novels

This list is by no means exhaustive; it does, however, include works which are representative of nodal points in the changing nature of nursing.

589 J J Abraham. *The Night Nurse*. 1913. Deals with contemporary worries; who were the new nurses, where did they come from, and how would their presence affect the lives and careers of the male doctors.
590 A Anderton. *Ruth*. 1952. Involves Florence Nightingale in the story.
591 J S Arey. *There Was No Yesterday*. 1943.
592 J S Arey. *Night Work*. nd.
593 C Bronte. *Shirley*. 1849. Introduces the 'trained' nurse, Zillah Horsfall, before Nightingale's reforms. Criticises the blind obedience expected of the nurse by the medical profession. Physically and in manners and habits, Horsfall bears strong likeness to Sarah Gamp, in Dickens (597).
595 R M Carey. *Merle's Crusade*. 1889. The story of one of the 'surplus' women, forced to earn her own living. She thinks about becoming a nurse but cannot afford the premium she thinks is necessary to train. Eventually becomes a children's nurse.
596 W Collins. *The New Magdalen*. 1873. A case of mistaken identity and deliberate deception; the nurse is a fallen woman—a prostitute—who goes to France during the Franco-Prussian War as a Red Cross nurse to seek salvation or even death. The contradictions of the 'lady with the lamp' and the prostitute are strong themes.
597 C Dickens. *Martin Chuzzlewit*. 1843/4. Infamous portrayal of pre-reformed nursing. Gave much ammunition to reformers and Dickens helped their case by claiming that he had known such women. Since that novel it has been difficult to reconstruct the sorts of nursing services and types of nurses available for the majority of the population; the myth has been so strong that Sarah has become 'real' and not a caricature.
598 E Drummond. *Scarlet Shadows*. 1978.
599 H Dudley. *The Hooded Falcon*. 1979. Story of a lady nurse with Nightingale at Scutari. The heroine becomes pregnant and this induces a softening in Nightingale's attitude towards her.
600 G Manville Fenn. *Nurse Elisia*. 1893. A lady nurse as hospital nurse and private nurse. Described by a village nurse, whom she displaces, as 'a nun dressed up for a holiday', the novel is about the problems of class when men and women from the same social group are placed in a work situation where they may be mutually dependent. Resolved by marriage

and by the nurse bowing to the doctor's authority, despite her education, upbringing and class.
601 E Gaskell. *Ruth*. 1853. A story of self-sacrifice and self-destruction brought about by the harmful influence of others. Ruth is a seamstress who is seduced by a 'gentleman'; the child is brought up in the home of a nonconformist family where Ruth is a governess. During an epidemic of fever—cholera—she becomes a nurse but she avoids the infection. When her lover returns she finds herself nursing him through his fever, which she catches and dies. While Nightingale approved of Ruth's experience as a fever nurse, the book was greeted badly by its audience. It is unlikely that Nightingale would have been too happy with the 'fallen woman' role either.
602 R Gordon. *The Private Life of Florence Nightingale*. 1978. Suggests an underlying stress of sexuality which helps to produce the Nightingale of Scutari and of the sick-bed. Sensationalist.
603 J Greenwood. *Humphrey Dyot*. 1867. About sick children.
604 E Grey. *The Little Beauty*. 1860. Concerned with a children's nurse.
605 Mrs Haycraft. *Sister Royal*. nd. Nurse in a children's home; marries the doctor.
606 A Mayhew. *Paved With Gold*. 1858. About sick wards.
607 H C Montgomerie. *Sister in Charge*. 1939.
608 F Murray. *The Burning Lamp*. 1923. The story of a 'Nightingale' who is interviewed by Nightingale and trained by Mrs Wardroper. Goes off to the American West as a 'missionary' for nursing.
609 L Prole. *The Greatest Nurse of Them All*. 1968. The Crimea again.
610 C Rayner. *Bedford Row*. 1977. Long saga (5 volumes); Crimea and Nightingale.
611 S Ridley. *Nurses and Ladies*. 1967. Uses and cites many sources for this novel of Nightingale.
612 C Terrot. *Miss Nightingale's Ladies*. 1948.
613 G Trelawney. *In a Cottage Hospital*. 1901. Two themes pursued in this novel; first, the state of administration and medical care in the many cottage hospitals of the period, and second, the dangers faced by young idealistic doctors in the working presence of attractive young nurses.
614 Mrs Humphrey Ward. *Marcella*. 1894. The problem of whether the middle class should become nurses or whether they should reform it from above, using their money and class.

9 FILM AS EVIDENCE

Reservations as to the use of fiction apply as strongly to film as to the printed book. It is 'permissible' to use film as evidence—newsreel or documentary film—since this is a newer form of communication and a step along from newspapers and journals; even when it is known that many 'realist' documentaries were reconstructions and not actual records, film continues to provide information for historians. Marwick has suggested, for example, that 'newsreel film of the suffragette agitation before the First World War sometimes gives a clearer insight into the sorts of things contemporaries found significant about the suffragette movement, than do surviving newspaper accounts.' (Marwick (656) p 17). Film, or at least some sorts of film, is as valuable a source as a newspaper, subject to the rigours of evaluation of any source of evidence. But, as noted, film should not be seen as evidence of facts or events which correspond to 'reality'; films are statements about attitudes and concerns.

9.1 Essays in criticism

615 M J Clark. (Ed). *Politics and the Media: Film and Television for the Political Scientist and Historian*. 1979.
616 *Historical Journal of Film, Radio and Television*. 1981–. Published twice a year, March and October. The first 4 volumes cover propaganda film of the Second World War.
617 R Low. *Films of Comment and Persuasion of the 1930s*. 1979. Excellent introduction to the use of film as evidence. Lists some films dealing with health and hospitals.
618 R Low. *Documentary and Educational Films of the 1930s*. Companion volume to 617.
619 C MacArthur. *Television and History*. 1978.
620 P Madden. (Ed). *Keeping Television Alive: the Television Work of the National Film Archive*. 1981. Catalogue of the NFI's collection.
621 E Oliver. (Ed). *Researcher's Guide to British Film and Television Collections*. 1981. Comprehensive list of institutions and their collections. Special categories listed. Has a useful discussion on the role of film as history.
622 K R M Short. *Feature Films as History*. 1981. Includes a discussion on how to use these films in historical analysis.

623 P Smith. *The Historian and Film*. 1976. Essential introduction to the topic.
624 P Sorlin. *The Film in History*. 1980. Good introduction to the difficulties of using film as evidence.

9.2 Films about doctors

625 The 'Doctor' Films; *Doctor in the House*. 1954.; *Doctor at Sea*. 1955.; *Doctor at Large*. 1957.; *Doctor in Love*. 1962.; *Doctor in Distress*. 1963.; *Doctor in Clover*. 1966.; *Doctor in Trouble*. 1970. Comedies.
626 *Men in White*. 1934. The tale of a young intern split between duty and love. (See 613).
627 *The New Interns*. 1964. 'Soap opera' comedy.
628 *Young Doctors*. 1961. Idealised treatment of the problems of the new doctor in a competitive world of medicine.

9.3 Films about nurses

629 *Dawn*. 1928. Silent film starring Sybil Thorndike as Edith Cavell, directed by Herbert Wilcox. Well-researched.
630 *The Feminine Touch*. 1956.
631 *Florence Nightingale*. 1915. Silent film.
632 *The Lady With The Lamp*. 1951.
633 *The Lamp Still Burns*. 1943. Film version of Dickens (445).
634 *Nurse Edith Cavell*. 1939. Wilcox's second attempt, this time starring Anna Neagle.
635 *Nurse on Wheels*. 1963. British mixture of comedy and pathos.
636 *Sister Kenny*. 1946. Serious film study of a polio nurse.
637 *Sixty Glorious Years*. 1938. Another Nightingale film.
638 *The White Angel*. 1936. Accurate although sentimental; Nightingale.

9.4 Films about patients and hospitals

639 *The National Health*. 1973. Based on Peter Nichols' play; a black comedy sending up other hospital films.
640 *Twice Round the Daffodils*. 1962. Life in a TB ward.
641 *White Corridors*. 1951. Big box-office success; life in a small Midlands hospital.

642 *I Never Promised You a Rose Garden*. 1979. A suicidal teenager in a mental hospital.
643 *Coma*. 1978. Thriller.
644 *Whose Life Is It, Anyway*? 1982.

10 PRIMARY SOURCES

In Section 1 the major differences between secondary and primary sources were discussed and Section 2 lists some of the main deposits which may need to be consulted for any study of the history of nursing or its contexts.

This sub-section lists those works which guide the researcher through the use of primary material or which give details of specific collections of primary data. Also included are some of the Parliamentary sources which have importance in nursing history.

10.1 Guides and reference works

645 British Film Institute. *Film and Television Drama on Offer*. Current volume 1982/3. Lists prices, distributors and addresses.
646 M F Bond. *Guide to the Records of Parliament*. 1971.
647 A F Comfort and C Loveless. (Compilers). *Guide to Government Data: A Survey of Unpublished Social Science Material in the Libraries of Government Departments in London*. 1974.
648 C Cook. *Sources in British Political History 1900–1951: Volume 1: A Guide to the Archives of Selected Organisations and Societies*. 1975.
649 P G Ford. *Select List of Parliamentary Papers 1833–1899*. 1953. Like other works by the Fords (see 650), this is essential as a guide to Parliamentary Papers of interest to the historian of nursing.
650 P and G Ford. *A Guide to Parliamentary Papers*. 1959. (1972).
651 J Foster and J Sheppard. *British Archives: A Guide to Archive Resources in the United Kingdom*. 1982. Very useful guide, although nursing items are rather unclear.
652 P Hepworth. *Archives and Manuscripts in Libraries*. 1964. Gives advice on the use of archives and lists some collections.
653 Imperial War Museum. *War Work 1914–1918: Oral History Re-*

cordings. 1978. Catalogued by S Brooks, the list includes recordings of VADs, ambulance drivers and military nurses.

654 D Iredale. *Enjoying Archives: What They Are, Where To Find Them, How To Use Them*. 1973. Excellent basic introduction to the topic, including a chapter on handwriting and the repair of documents.

656 A Marwick. *Primary Sources*. 1970. Open University: Humanities Foundation Course Unit 6: *Introduction to History. Part 2*. A useful guide and series of exercises in the identification, evaluation and use of primary sources.

657 S L Mayer and W J Koenig. *The Two World Wars: A Guide to Manuscript Collections in the United Kingdom*. 1976.

658 National Register of Archives. *List of Accessions to Repositories*. Annually published.

659 W R Powell. *Local History from Blue Books: A Select List of Sessional Papers of the House of Commons*. 1962.

660 Public Record Office. *Guide to the Contents of the Public Record Office*. 1980. Volume 2, first published 1963, includes references to the Ministry of Health and the Papers of the General Nursing Council, Medical and Nursing Service Papers 1899–1900, and so on.

661 R Storey and L Madden. *Primary Sources for Victorian Studies: A Guide to the Location and Use of Unpublished Materials*. 1977. Very handy 'pocket' guide to the topic.

662 P Thompson. The BBC Archives: Oral History. *Oral History*, 1. 1973. A guide to some of the taperecordings made by the BBC of interest to the historian to publication date.

663 T R Thomson. *A Catalogue of British Family Histories*. 1928, reprinted 1976.

10.2 Parliamentary Papers

The following are just a few of the many Parliamentary Papers and non-Parliamentary reports which you may find it useful to consult for a project in the history of nursing; for others see (649) above.

664 Mismanagement of the Sick Poor: Paddington Workhouse. *Parliamentary Papers*, 1866, lxi. A Select Committee Report in the wake of the Timothy Daly case. See White (441).

665 Select Committee on the Metropolitan Hospitals. *Parliamentary Papers*, 1890/1, xiii.
666 Nursing the Sick Poor in Workhouses. *Parliamentary Papers*, 1902, xxxviii. Minutes of Evidence, 1902, xxxix.
667 Registration of Nurses. *Parliamentary Papers*, 1904, vi.
668 Registration of Nurses. *Parliamentary Papers*, 1905, vii.
669 Royal Commission on the Poor Laws. *Parliamentary Papers*, 1909, Report xxxvii; Minutes of Evidence from some major nursing figures, xl; see also volume xlv for a discussion of the overlap in London between the voluntary and Poor Law medical services.
670 Public Health and Social Conditions. *Parliamentary Papers*, 1909, ciii. Includes a report from Newsholme, Chief Medical Officer at the time.
671 The Workings of the Midwives Act 1902. *Parliamentary Papers*, 1909, xxxiii.
672 Report of the Chief Medical Officer: Sir Arthur Newsholme 1917–1918. *Parliamentary Papers*, 1918, xi.
673 The Future Provision of Medical and Allied Services Consultative Committee: Interim Report. *Parliamentary Papers*, 1920, xvii.
674 The Voluntary Hospitals Committee. *Parliamentary Papers*, 1921, xiii.
675 The Administration of Public Mental Hospitals. *Parliamentary Papers*, 1922, viii.
676 Nursing in County and Borough Mental Hospitals. Departmental Committee, *Non-Parliamentary Papers/Board of Control*, 1924.
677 The Lancet Commission on the Recruitment and Training of Nurses: Final Report. *The Lancet*, 1932, volume 1.
678 The Training of Nurses: Scottish Department Committee. *Parliamentary Papers*, 1935/6, xi.
679 Inter-Departmental Committee on Nursing Services. *Non-Parliamentary Papers/Ministry of Health and the Board of Education*, 1939. The Athlone Committee; see Baly (424) for a discussion.
680 Nurses Salaries Committee: Salaries and Emoluments of Female Nurses. *Parliamentary Papers*, 1942/3, v The Rushcliffe Committee; see Abel-Smith (422) for a discussion.
681 A National Health Service: A Statement. *Parliamentary Papers*, 1943/4, viii.

682 Mental Nursing and the Nursing of Mentally Defectives: Inter-Departmental Nursing Services Committee Sub-Committee. *Non-Parliamentary Papers/Ministry of Health and the Ministry of Education*, 1945.

683 The Hospitals Survey 1945. *Non-Parliamentary Papers/Ministry of Health*, 1946.

684 Working Party on the Recruitment and Training of Nurses. *Non-Parliamentary Papers/Ministry of Health, Department of Health (Scotland) and the Ministry of Labour*, 1947. The Wood Report; see Baly (424) for a discussion. A Minority Report by Cohen, 1948, argued for an increase in trained nurse establishments based on bed occupancy and usage rates.

Section 3
Useful addresses

Nursing and medical

Charing Cross Medical School Reynolds Building St Dunstan's Road London W6 8PP	Has a collection of nursing records.
City and Hackney Health Authority St Bartholomew's Hospital West Smithfield London EC1A 7BE	Holds most of the records of this hospital including nursing records.
Contemporary Medical Archives Centre Wellcome Institute for the History of Medicine 183 Euston Road London NW1 2BP	Some nursing material and guides to other collections.
Glasgow University Archives University of Glasgow Glasgow G12 8QQ	Records from hospitals in the Glasgow area, including mental hospitals.
Glasgow University Library Department of Special Collections Hillhead Street Glasgow G12 8QE	
The Middlesex Hospital Mortimer Street London W1N 5AA	Includes the registers of nurses 1867–.

Oxford Health Authority Archives
The Warneford Hospital
Warneford Lane
Headington
Oxford OX3 7JX

Very useful collection of archive material relating to psychiatric hospitals.

St George's Hospital Archive Department
Room 60 Grosvenor Wing
St George's Hospital
Blackshaw Road
Tooting
London SW17

General Register Office for Scotland
New Register House
Edinburgh
EH1 3YT

Has records of births, marriages and deaths in Scotland 1855– as well as parish records pre-1855. There are also important nursing archives, including material relating to the registration of nurses. See C Maggs, The Register of Nurses in the Scottish Poor Law Service 1885–1919. *Nursing Times*, 77, 33, 25 November 1981.

Greater London Record Office
40 Northampton Road
London EC1

Important collection of Nightingale papers.

House of Lords Record Office
House of Lords
London SW1A OPW

Imperial War Museum
Lambeth Road
London SE1 6HZ

India Office Library and Records
Foreign and Colonial Office
197 Blackfriars Road
London SE1 8NG

Important collection of papers relevant to the history of nursing and to health. For a guide to the collection see, W Foster. *Guide to the India Office Records 1600–1858, 1919–1966: List of Publications in Print.* 1977.

Modern Records Centre
University of Warwick Library
University of Warwick
Coventry
CV4 7AL

National Register of Archives
Quality House
Quality Court
Chancery Lane
London WC2A 1HP

Others

British Association for Local History
43 Bedford Square
London WC1B 3DP

British Library
Department of Manuscripts
Great Russell Street
London WC1B 3DG

British Library
Newspaper Library
Colindale Avenue
London NW9 5HE

British Library
Reference Division
Department of Printed Books
Great Russell Street
London WC1B 3DG

Business Archives Council
Dominion House
37–45 Tooley Street
London Bridge
London SE1 2QF

Business Records Association
The Charterhouse
Charterhouse Square
London EC1M 6AU

City of London Polytechnic
Old Castle Street
London E1 7NT

Contains the Fawcett Library.

General Register Office
(Northern Ireland)
49–55 Chichester Street
Belfast
BT1 4HL

Has the records of births, marriages and deaths in Northern Ireland 1922–

King Edward's Hospital Fund for London
King's Fund Centre
126 Albert Street
London NW1 7NF

National Register of Archives (Scotland)
PO Box 36
HM General Register House
Edinburgh
EH1 3YY

Office of Population Censuses and Surveys General Register Office St Catherine's House 10 Kingsway London WC2B 6JP	Births, marriages and deaths 1837–
Peter Liddle's 1914–18 Personal Experiences Archives Sunderland Polytechnic St Mary's Building Chester Road Sunderland SR1 3SD	A unique collection of oral evidence from the period as well as several thousand books.
Public Record Office Ruskin Avenue Kew Richmond Surrey TW9 4DU Public Record Office Chancery Lane London WC2A 1LR	The two offices are gradually merging; it is worthwhile writing to ask which office holds the collections you are interested in.
Public Record Office (Northern Ireland) Law Courts Building May Street Belfast BT1 3JJ	
Royal College of Nursing 20 Cavendish Square London W1M 0AB	

Royal Commission on Historical Manuscripts
Quality House
Quality Court
Chancery Lane
London WC2A 1HP

Society of Friends' Library
Friends' House
Euston Road
London NW1 2BJ

University of Nottingham Library
Manuscript Department
University of Nottingham
University Park
Notts NG7 2RD

Some archive material relevant to the history of nursing.

Wellcome Institute for the History of Medicine
183 Euston Road
London NW1 2BP

Index